American Art at Harvard

American Art at Harvard

Fogg Art Museum   Harvard University

Exhibition held at the Fogg Art Museum

April 19–June 18, 1972

Cover illustration:

Alvan Fisher

View of Harvard Yard (detail) (No. 34)

1500 copies of the catalogue

designed by Malcolm Grear Designers

type set by Craftsman Type Inc.

have been printed by Meriden Gravure Co.

on Mohawk Superfine

in April 1972

on the occasion of the exhibition

American Art at Harvard

Foreword

The ambitious scope of *American Art at Harvard* is due in large measure to the enthusiasm of Kenyon C. Bolton, III, who conceived the idea of this first general survey of Harvard's holdings in American art and found energetic collaborators among fellow graduate students in Fine Arts, Peter G. Huenink, Earl A. Powell, III, Harry Z. Rand, and Nanette Sexton. The interest of these five students in a field that has never occupied center stage at the Fogg has been stimulated and encouraged by Benjamin Rowland, Jr. Professor Rowland may be startled, but we hope pleased, to read the dedication.

Daniel Robbins, *Director*

This exhibition was dedicated from its inception to Professor
Benjamin Rowland, Jr., who is personally responsible for the
advanced study of the visual arts of America at Harvard.
His extensive knowledge, quiet encouragement, and unfailing
energy have inspired a new generation of art historians.

At a time when American art went unrespected, when indeed it was barely respectable, Benjamin Rowland made it a vital and a lively discipline. If he had done no more than to introduce the art of our country to a succession of undergraduate and graduate students, he would have performed an uncommon and invaluable service. But of course he did much more. He made one see the immense possibilities of the field, and did so with an insight and a wit that left an indelible stamp upon those who were privileged to have worked with him. My gratitude to him is immeasurable, and it is a rare pleasure to be able to express it so openly and publicly on this occasion of well-deserved tribute.

Nicolai Cikovsky, Jr.
Associate Professor and Director of the Art Gallery
Vassar College, Poughkeepsie, New York

I suppose I was one of the first students to concentrate in the field of American art under the warm guidance of Ben Rowland. Actually, Ben was teacher and mentor in all three fields of my greatest interest — American art, Late Italian Medieval, and Oriental, although in reverse order. I mention this because, in addition to his guidance as a teacher — strong yet free — he, more than any of my teachers, demonstrated the meaningfulness of interrelationships between seemingly totally distinct areas of art history, which in turn has became an important aspect of my own art historical pursuits. It was put into practice early, too, when I was honored to work as a teaching fellow under him at Harvard. These experiences with Ben Rowland were my most meaningful during my years in Graduate School; all of us in the field of American art owe him tremendous gratitude.

William H. Gerdts
Assistant Professor of Art
Brooklyn College

When I came to Harvard as a graduate student in 1953, I had never taken a course in American art. Benjamin Rowland's undergraduate course on that subject, which I audited, convinced me that American art would be one of my major fields of scholarly interest. I was taken by his absolute command of the subject, his keen sense for artistic quality, and his understated humor. In this course and in his graduate seminars, he showed how American art reflected the main currents of Western European (and sometimes Oriental) art, and in doing so he warned us against overvaluing the provincial art of our native country. Yet he also believed that American art was worthy of serious study, and he demonstrated how the scholarly apparatus of European (and Oriental) art history could be applied to good effect. His teaching and methods of scholarship have been a model to me and, I am sure, to many others fortunate enough to have studied with him.

William Innes Homer
Chairman, Department of Art History
University of Delaware

Respect for one's professor, though not uncommon, is rarely joined to an affection that allows him to survive in one's memory as a colleague, a guide whose voice often interrupts and adds to those dialogues with oneself that academics are so prone to. So whenever I meet Ben Rowland, I have the pleasure of meeting someone very familiar — though we often don't meet for years. A rare courage caused Ben Rowland to take on a field widely scorned by his colleagues. An unusual teacher, he allowed his students to develop the best of their potential, without imposing his special interests. The great teacher teaches not so much through content, as through example. Rowland's exemplary mind, when applied to the problems of American art, instructed his students in the intellectual disciplines that would rescue the field from the stigma of "Americana." He saw American art in a broad cultural context, rather than confined to the usual art historical vacuum. He thus encouraged a whole new generation of American art historians to approach the field with the same intellectual rigor as the rest of world art history. It is a pleasure for me to acknowledge this here, and I thank those at the Fogg who made it possible for me to do so.

Barbara Novak
Chairman, Department of Art History
Barnard College, Columbia University

Benjamin Rowland possesses wide-ranging intellectual interests and a unique gift for classroom communication. His effectiveness as a teacher is enhanced by his ability to temper pedagogical concern with restraint, allowing each student to work out his own problems, injecting just the right dose of encouragement, admonition or advice as needed. I am grateful to him as beneficiary of his teaching talents, received both in class and in personal and professional guidance through the intricacies of writing a dissertation. Moreover, I appreciate those special Ben Rowland influences, sneaky and pervasive, that became a permanent part of my art historical baggage when I left Harvard. Sneaky in that I cannot prevent myself, even now, from envisioning Albert P. Ryder or Guido da Siena as robed Orientals; pervasive in that the lesson he taught me from the start was that art history can be fun. And it is!

Jules D. Prown
Director, Paul Mellon Center for British Art, and British Studies
Yale University

In an age of pretentious programs which encourage over-specialization, Ben Rowland stands out as an 18th-century man. Like Charles Willson Peale, he does nearly everything well; a painter, a collector, a great scholar who is equally at home with classical, Asian, or European style, he creates respect for American art simply by including it in his repertoire. He teaches mainly by his own example, for he knows that the love of objects and the methods of scholarship can be learned in many ways, on many timetables. With gentleness and sympathy, he encourages each student to stand alone while expanding to his own full growth.

Theodore E. Stebbins, Jr.
Curator of American Painting and Sculpture
Yale University Art Gallery

Known foremost for his work in Oriental and Medieval art, Ben Rowland has also inspired more than one generation of students in American art. He has taught this special group with quiet energy, good humor, and ready encouragement. If he can take pride in what we have done because of his initiative, we can certainly be proud of what we learned from him. I am honored and grateful to join others in both personal and professional tribute.

John Wilmerding
Chairman, Department of Art
Dartmouth College

Preface

This exhibition is not designed to illustrate the history and growth of the Fogg Museum Collections, but rather to bring to light the scores of objects which, over the period of many years, have found their way into divers parts of the University. Some of these works have been long hidden away or on loan and not easily accessible to the public, while others, little known and rarely exhibited, are owned by other Departments of the University.

Few people are aware of the great collection of paintings of American Indian life, including a superb Caleb Bingham, in the Bushnell Collection at the Peabody Museum, or of the originals and copies of Charles Bird King and Catlin in the same institution. Another interesting rarity is the copy by John Trumbull of Smibert's replica of Van Dyke's portrait of Cardinal Bentivoglio. The Smibert copy, now lost, was a veritable school for Boston painters when it hung in his studio during the eighteenth century.

Collecting works of art by the University was rare until the end of the nineteenth century with the opening of the first Fogg Museum in 1895. Occasional bequests found their way to the college in the eighteenth century in addition to commissions for life portraits of George Washington and of Harvard notables. Many of these are contained in the Harvard Portrait Collection, which is rich in works by John Singleton Copley, Robert Feke, Rembrandt Peale, Edward Savage, and others.

The graduate students who have assembled this exhibition have found hidden treasures in literally every corner of the University. The earliest portrait comes from the Medical School, and many notable masterpieces ranging from Feke to Fitz Hugh Lane have been loaned by the Law School and the Business School. It should be noted that the Fogg's policy of lending works of art for decorative purposes to various University buildings has in some cases resulted in damage or loss of valuable works, including a superb Copley, through the careless custodianship of the borrowers.

Benjamin Rowland, Jr.

Introduction

Little in the way of documentary evidence exists to show that likenesses were made in New England in the seventeenth century, but Harvard College accounts for the year 1680 record payment made to Major Thomas Smith for work done for the Corporation:

Colledge Dr to money pd Major Tho. Smith for drawing Dr. Ames effigies pr Order of Corporation £ 4.4

Since the early records of patronage, the continuity of Harvard's interest in American art has been, in harmony with the fluctuations of national taste, eccentric and often unsympathetic. The strength of the University's collection is still its portrait holdings, because, for the most part, these objects were acquired with only a secondary consideration for their purely esthetic worth. This exhibition marks the first time that American art at Harvard has been brought together in a comprehensive exhibition, and it would be desirable if this venture initiated a methodical study and fostered an appreciation of American art.

Many of these works have never been shown publicly, others are world-famous, some accent particular high spots of the collection, all contribute to the newly-emergent awareness of the unique problems of culture in the New World.

Spanning four centuries, the Harvard Collections grew by accretion rather than as a protracted campaign of taste. The holdings were never organized to be an indicator of America's visual history. With the exception of the William Hayes Fogg Bequest, the Grenville L. Winthrop Bequest, and the acquisitions of the Louise E. Bettens Fund for the Purchase of American Art, the collection represents the sum of individual gifts and corporation commissions.

The collection as a whole is uneven; important artists go unrepresented; periods are thinly illustrated; and major talents must be regarded in terms of secondary works. The appearance of disjunction in the catalogue reflects the current state of the collection. Space and funding have precluded a consideration of printmaking, photography, and architecture.

Until recent years American art was considered to be specifically derivative of European art movements. The position that American art was inferior to its European models is in the process of reconsideration. This exhibition is presented to encourage a climate in which further speculation in problems in American art can be carried out.

The preparation for the show could not have been accomplished without the good will and enthusiasm of many people during the last twelve months. We should like to thank especially the participating institutions and individuals who have shown great generosity in loaning to the show the paintings and sculptures in their care: Mr. Stephen Williams of the Peabody Museum, Dean Albert

M. Sacks of the Law School, Dean and Mrs. Lawrence Fouraker and Mr. Robert Lovett of the Business School, Dean Robert H. Ebert and Mr. Harold Bloomquist of the Medical School, Dean Krister Stendahl and Mrs. Elinor Thompson of the Divinity School, Professor Alfred W. Crompton of the Agassiz Museum, Dr. William Bond and Miss Carolyn R. Jakeman of Houghton Library, W. C. Burriss Young of the Faculty Club, Kenneth Andrews of Leverett House, Professor Bruce Chalmers of Winthrop House, Mr. Paul A. Freund of the Society of Fellows, Professor William Liller of Adams House, Professor Arthur Smithies of Kirkland House, Mr. Douglas Bryant of the University Library, Professor John Coolidge, Dr. J. Maltzburger, Mrs. Peter I. B. Lavan, Mr. and Mrs. John P. Spiegel, Mr. Robert Shenton, the Secretary to the Corporation, and especially President and Mrs. Derek Bok.

Mrs. Arthur Brooks and Mrs. P. D. Shaplin deserve special thanks for their enthusiasm and assistance on behalf of the show. As always, the entire Fogg staff has provided many hours of assistance. We are especially grateful to Mrs. Peter Ambler, Curator of the Harvard University Portrait Collection, whose knowledge of the collections and whose unflagging efforts have made possible the gathering together of this material.

The catalogue has been enriched by contributions from Alice Jackson Myers, Katharyn Reiser, and John R. Lane in their areas of expertise. We are especially grateful to John T. Kirk for adding his knowledge to the work started by Page Talbot in identifying and cataloguing a selection of the American furniture at Harvard. John Wilmerding most generously read the manuscript and made valuable editorial suggestions.

Grants from the National Endowment for the Arts and the Stebbins Fund, Inc. are responsible in part for the mounting of the exhibition and the publishing of the catalogue.

    Kenyon C. Bolton, III
    Peter G. Huenink
    Earl A. Powell, III
    Harry Z. Rand
    Nanette Sexton

Unknown artist

1 *Dr. John Clark,* 1664

Oil on canvas, 34½ x 27⅛ inches

Inscribed center left: Aetatis Suae; and center right: 66 Anno 1664

Provenance: Dr. John Clark, sitter (d. 1664); Dr. John Clark (d. 1690); Dr. John Clark (d. 1728); Dr. John Clark (d. 1768); Mrs. Simeon (Elizabeth Clark) Howard (d. 1777); Dr. John Clark Howard (d. 1810); Dr. John Clark Howard (d. 1844); Boston Medical Library in the Countway Library of Medicine, Harvard Medical School, Gift of Mrs. S. W. Pickering and Miss H. S. Howard through the Massachusetts Historical Society, 1901.

Bibliography: J. Thacher, *American Medical Biography,* I, Boston, 1828, 222; L. Dresser, ed., *XVIIth Century Painting in New England* [exhibition catalogue], Worcester Art Museum, Worcester, Mass., 1935, 51-53, fig. 50; S. M. Gold, "A Study in Early Boston Portrait Attributions: Augustine Clement, Painter-Stainer of Reading, Berkshire, and Massachusetts Bay," *Old-Time New England,* 58, 1968, 61-78.

Dr. John Clark (1598?–1664) was among the first English surgeons to emigrate to Massachusetts. He lived initially in Newbury and later in Boston. Of the two surgical tools shown in his portrait, that above is a trephine, most often used to remove discs of bone from the skull; the one below is a Hey's saw, a narrow instrument employed in bone operations.

This is one of the first portraits painted in New England. Its solidity and realism link it to Dutch portraiture. The inscriptions "Aetatis Suae" on the left, and on the right "66 Anno 1664" (in his age 66, in the year 1664) place the work in the genre of British provincial portraits of the Elizabethan era. The canvas has been attributed to the Boston painter-stainer Augustine Clement, a neighbor of Dr. Clark. However, no documentary evidence has been found linking Clement to this portrait or to that of any other New Englander. It also seems strange that Clement would suddenly resume portraiture almost thirty years after his emigration from Berkshire. Finally, none of his works painted in England before his departure exist to form the basis of a stylistic comparison with the likeness of Dr. Clark. But the relative sophistication of this painting, as opposed to a native primitive like the *Cotton Tufts* (No. 27) suggests an artist trained in a studio tradition. Perhaps this artist came from England but lived only a short time in Massachusetts, for his style certainly had little impact on the work of his colonial successors.

KDR

Unknown artist

2 *William Stoughton,* ca. 1700

Oil on canvas, 50¼ x 42 inches

Provenance: William Stoughton; inherited (?) by his niece, Mrs. Mehitable Cooper; Cooper family; Harvard University Portrait Collection, Gift of John Cooper, 1810 (H 37).

Bibliography: L. Dresser, ed., *XVIIth Century Painting in New England* [exhibition catalogue], Worcester Art Museum, Worcester, Mass., 1935, 144-147, fig. 145; L. Huntsinger, *Harvard Portraits* (A. Burroughs, ed.), Cambridge, Mass., 1936, 130.

This portrait of William Stoughton (1631–1701) is one of the oldest American paintings in the Harvard University Portrait Collection and is an important document relating to the early years of Harvard College. Stoughton, who graduated from Harvard in 1650, became a powerful man in Massachusetts. As chief magistrate in the Salem witchcraft trials of 1692, he, with his obstinate, overbearing attitude, was largely responsible for their tragic outcome. He served as Lieutenant Governor of Massachusetts from 1692 until his death in 1701.

The three-quarter-length portrait represents Stoughton attired in a dark gown with elaborate fastenings and a brown cape with a dull red-orange lining. His highly articulated elbow is draped as if clewed. His palm is turned upward in a solicitous gesture. The naive composition and figure style indicate that the artist of this work had a second-hand knowledge of Dutch portraiture and suggest also that he may have known the work of the painter of the Gibbs-Freake portraits (Dresser, *XVIIth Century Painting,* 176).

Through the rectangular aperture to the left is an improbable landscape of cone-shaped hills. Displayed prominently against this background is Stoughton Hall, the gift of William Stoughton to Harvard. Stoughton Hall was built about 1700, but was taken down in 1780. Presumably this portrait was painted soon after its construction, the painting serving to commemorate the event.

PH

Unknown artist

3   *Council of Ministers,* ca. 1744

Oil on panel, 30⅜ x 41½ inches

Provenance: Painted for John Lowell, ca. 1744; purchased by T. W. Higginson for James Russell Lowell, Elmwood, 1850-51; A. Kingsley Porter, Elmwood; bequeathed to Dr. Francis L. Burnett and Mrs. Esther Lowell Cunningham; Harvard University, Gift of Dr. Francis L. Burnett and Mrs. Esther Lowell Cunningham (1964.27).

Bibliography: J. J. Currier, *Ould Newbury,* Boston, 1896, 451; L. Karr, "A Council of Ministers," *Antiques,* 11, 1927, 45-46, fig. 45; A. Burroughs, "An Early Overmantle," *Art in America,* 29, 1941, 227-229, fig. opp. 233; N. Little, *American Decorative Wall Painting: 1700-1850,* Sturbridge, Mass., 1952, 46, fig. 47.

The *Council of Ministers* is an overmantle panel, crude and unorthodox, from the house of Rev. John Lowell (1704–1767) of Newburyport. The integration of the disparate scenes may once have been served by a tree, remnants of which have been abraded nearly out of existence. To the right, seven ministers are seated in an alcove with John Lowell at the head of the table, a format reminiscent of English tavern signs. The arch bears the inscription: "In necessariis, unitas; in non-necessariis, libertas; in utrisque, charitas" (In essentials, unity; in nonessentials, liberty; in both, charity). To the left of the group is a mysteriously symbolic landscape (Burroughs, "An Early Overmantle," 228).

The panel's subject was inspired by a council of churches convened in Newburyport on 24 July 1744 to deal with a schism precipitated by the preachings of the evangelist George Whitefield. Through its long association with the Lowell family, the panel is thought to commemorate the Rev. John Lowell's reconciliatory efforts. The work clearly holds more historical than artistic interest, especially as one of the very few pictures of the mideighteenth century in which a figure group has been painted in definite historical circumstances.

PH

Attributed to **Joseph Badger** 1708–1765

4 *Rev. George Whitefield,* ca. 1743–1765

Oil on canvas, 42 x 32⅞ inches

Provenance: Mrs. Warters; Harvard University Portrait Collection, Gift of Mrs. H. P. Oliver, 1852 (H 27).

Bibliography: L. Park, "Joseph Badger, 1708–1765, and a Descriptive List of Some of His Works," Massachusetts Historical Society, *Proceedings,* 51, 1918, 158-201; A. Burroughs, *Limners and Likenesses,* Cambridge, Mass., 1936, 51, 59, fig. 42; L. Huntsinger, *Harvard Portraits* (A. Burroughs, ed.), Cambridge, Mass., 1936, 145-146.

This portrait of Rev. George Whitefield (1714–1770), English evangelist and spellbinding religious orator, is thought to have been painted by the Boston limner Joseph Badger. The powerful image with its naive realism, knife-edge modeling, and good design suggests Badger's authorship and recalls his portrait of *Mrs. Jonathan Edwards* in the Boston Museum of Fine Arts. Badger was born in Charlestown, Massachusetts, and his oeuvre, mainly portraits dating from 1743, has yet to be fully assessed.

The donor of the portrait, Mrs. H. P. Oliver, traced the picture to "a Mrs. Warters who was intimately acquainted with Whitefield and I have heard her say that it was an excellent likeness" (Huntsinger, *Harvard Portraits,* 146). Whitefield's revivalist preachings caused the defection of many parishioners in Newburyport, an indignation that led eventually to Rev. John Lowell's *Council of Ministers* (No. 3).

PH

Robert Feke 1705/10–after 1750

5 *Isaac Royall and His Family*, 1741

Oil on canvas, 56⅜₁₆ x 77¾ inches

Signed on back: 1741/by Robert/Feke

Provenance: Harvard Law School, Harvard University Portrait Collection, Gift of Dr. George Stevens Jones, 1879 (H 159).

Bibliography: H. Foote, *Robert Feke*, Cambridge, Mass., 1930, 88-89, 103-104, 179-183; A. Burroughs, *Limners and Likenesses*, Cambridge, Mass., 1936, 43, 44, 51, 52, fig. 37; L. Huntsinger, *Harvard Portraits* (A. Burroughs, ed.), Cambridge, Mass., 1936, 117.

The portrait of the Royall family, painted in 1741, is one of the earliest attempts at group portraiture in colonial America. Its composition is strongly derivative of John Smibert's *Dean George Berkeley and His Entourage* of 1729, now in the Yale University Art Gallery, and x-ray examination reveals evidence of struggle and correction in the design. The baby is a later addition, perhaps by Greenwood, inserted probably after Feke had moved Penelope Royall, who is second from the left, several inches to the right (Burroughs, *Limners and Likenesses*, 45, 59). Despite relative compositional and technical weaknesses, Feke's group portrait is unquestionably the masterpiece of his early career. The picture combines structural strength and naive elegance, making it a splendid example of the socially elaborate idiom that was American portraiture of this time.

On the back of the canvas, now hidden by relining fabric, an inscription identifies the figures around the carpet-covered table:

> *Drawn for*
> *Mr. Isaac Royall whose*
> *Portrait is on the foreside*
> *Age 22 years 13th instant*
> *His lady in blue*
> *Aged 19 years 13th instant*
> *Her Sister Miss Mary Palmer in red*
> *Aged 18 years 2nd of August*
> *His sister Penelope Royall in green*
> *Aged 17 years in April*
> *The child his daughter Elizabeth*
> *Aged 8 months 7th instant*
> *Finisht Sept. 15th 1741*
> *by Robert Feke.*

Isaac Royall, Jr. (1719–1781), who appears in the painting at the head of the table, was the son of a wealthy merchant who came to Medford, Massachusetts, from Antigua. The younger Royall's bequest led to the establishment of the first professorship of law at Harvard.

PH

John Singleton Copley 1738–1815

6 *Dorothy Murray,* ca. 1758–1761

Oil on canvas, 36¼ x 28⅛ inches

Provenance: Fogg Art Museum, Harvard University, Gift of Mrs. David Simmons (1929.321).

Bibliography: B. Parker and A. Wheeler, *John Singleton Copley: American Portraits,* Boston, 1938, 137-138, pl. 36; J. Prown, *John Singleton Copley,* Cambridge, Mass., 1966, I, 34, 36, fig. 96.

Born in Boston in 1738, Copley is usually credited with the development of a forceful native realism which marks him as the greatest portrait painter in colonial America.

His portrait of Dorothy Murray (1745–1811) represents her in a golden-brown dress with a flowered stomacher that reads visually like an ornamental breastplate. Indications of style, such as the darkened background, the subdued colors, and the strong value contrasts, relate this portrait to what Prown defines as the period of Copley's early maturity, 1758–1761. Dorothy Murray's daughter later recalled that her mother was sixteen years old at the time of this portrait, which would date it 1761 (S. Leslie, *Recollections of My Mother,* Boston, 1886, 69). The portrait has been much damaged in the past: there are numerous losses and the paint has been abraded extensively in the thin darks of her drapery, in the hair, and in the background.

PH

John Singleton Copley

7 *Mrs. Thomas Boylston,* 1766

Oil on canvas, 50⅝ x 40¼ inches

Signed middle right: Jnᵒ S. Copley/pinx 1766

Provenance: Harvard University Portrait Collection, Bequest of Ward Nicholas Boylston, 1828 (H 16).

Bibliography: L. Huntsinger, *Harvard Portraits* (A. Burroughs, ed.), Cambridge, Mass., 1936, 25-26; J. Prown, *John Singleton Copley* [exhibition catalogue], National Gallery of Art, Washington, D.C., The Metropolitan Museum of Art, New York, Museum of Fine Arts, Boston, 1965, 44, 49, 137, colorplate IV; J. Prown, *John Singleton Copley,* Cambridge, Mass., 1966, I, fig. 178.

8 *Nicholas Boylston,* 1767

Oil on canvas, 49 x 40 inches

Signed lower left: J S in monogram within a C and the date, 1767

Provenance: Harvard University Portrait Collection, Bequest of Ward Nicholas Boylston, 1828 (H 90).

Bibliography: L. Huntsinger, *Harvard Portraits* (A. Burroughs, ed.), Cambridge, Mass., 1936, 23-24; J. Prown, *John Singleton Copley* [exhibition catalogue], National Gallery of Art, Washington, D.C., The Metropolitan Museum of Art, New York, Museum of Fine Arts, Boston, 1965, 48-49, 137, fig. 48; J. Prown, *John Singleton Copley,* Cambridge, Mass., 1966, I, fig. 182.

Copley's Boylston portraits belong to the period of his greatest popularity as a social portraitist in Boston. Painted in 1766 and 1767, they are among the best portraits of Copley's later Boston period, a time when he was beginning to measure his work against contemporary European standards.

The painting of Mrs. Boylston (d. 1774) is one of a series of portraits that Copley made of society matrons and, through its slakened intensity and rounded modeling, represents a distinct departure from his earlier attempts at stylish portraiture. The wife of Thomas Boylston, a Boston merchant, and the mother of Nicholas Boylston, she is represented here in a three-quarter-length pose seated in a chair upholstered with silk damask. Copley's handling of her gown demonstrates his flair for capturing the effects of fine satin. One

overlooked aspect of this familiar portrait is that the hands were never finished; they show in excellent fashion Copley's procedure in building up the skeletal structure and flesh details. Another disquieting aspect is the wooden, curiously detached quality of the arm that holds a silk mitt. Copley's use of restrained color and his thorough devotion to the sitter's likeness, as seen in the small, highlighted face, are in harmony with the personality of this unmistakable, though restrained, *grande dame.*

One year after Copley painted the portrait of Mrs. Boylston, he made the portrait of her son, Nicholas Boylston (1716–1771), founder of the Boylston Professorship of Rhetoric and Oratory. In formal terms, the picture is closely akin to that of Mrs. Boylston, exhibiting a lessening of intensity as compared with previous works. Copley achieved this relaxation by moving the figure of Boylston closer to the picture plane. He is shown with a genial smile as he sits, legs crossed, in a Chippendale chair. Complementing the spontaneity of the entire conception is the turban he wears instead of a formal wig on his shaved head.

The image of Nicholas Boylston is by no means courtly, yet it unmistakably presents a social portrait of a prominent Bostonian. Elements symbolizing the Boston merchant's role in society are included in the picture. His left arm rests casually on two leather-bound books, the lower one with the word LEDGE(R) written on the binding. Through the deep red curtain which forms a diagonal to the upper-right-hand corner can be seen a distant view with a lighthouse and a small square-rigged vessel riding the waves.

In 1772, one year after Boylston's death, the Harvard Corporation commissioned Copley to paint a full-length posthumous portrait of him. Copley executed the commission using this three-quarter-length portrait as his model. The full-length portrait (H 20) now hangs at the Medical School in Countway Library.

PH

John Singleton Copley

9 *John Adams,* 1783

Oil on canvas, 93¾ x 57¹⁵⁄₁₆ inches

Provenance: John Singleton Copley; Adams family; Harvard University Portrait Collection, Bequest of Ward Nicholas Boylston, 1828 (H 74).

Bibliography: *Letters and Papers of John Singleton Copley and Henry Pelham,* Massachusetts Historical Society, Boston, 1914, 374; L. Huntsinger, *Harvard Portraits* (A. Burroughs, ed.), Cambridge, Mass., 1936, 7; J. Prown, *John Singleton Copley,* Cambridge, Mass., 1966, II, 388, fig. 438; A. Oliver, *Portraits of John and Abigail Adams,* Cambridge, Mass., 1967, 23-38, fig. 9.

Copley was acutely aware of the constraints his provincial environment placed upon the practice of his profession, and at the urging of Benjamin West and Sir Joshua Reynolds, he left Boston for Europe in 1774, never to return. A chalk drawing of Adams in the Metropolitan Museum of Art, New York, served as a preliminary study for this work which was painted toward the end of 1783, when Adams was in London serving as the First Minister to the Court of St. James.

Judging from this life-size portrait of John Adams (1735–1826), one can see that the world of London portraiture has imposed some constraints on Copley. While the portrait is an amalgam of Copley's mature skill and English stylishness, the spontaneity and directness of his late Boston portraits are no longer present. Adams' pose is stereotyped, and the trappings which surround him are labored and prosaic. Adams himself was self-conscious about its aristocratic appearance. Copley, however, was aware of its possibilities as a source for engravings and kept the Adams portrait in his possession for thirty-four years (Oliver, *Portraits,* 29).

John Quincy Adams wrote to Copley from St. Petersburg in April of 1811: "It is the only full-length picture of my father, as large as life, that has ever been painted, and perhaps the only one that will remain after him." This is only the second time this picture, well known as it is through innumerable photographs and engravings, has been included in a formal exhibition, the first time being in 1796 at the Royal Academy in London.

PH

John Singleton Copley

10 *Colonels Hugo and Schlepegrell,* 1787

Oil on canvas, 26 x 22 inches

Provenance: Lyndhurst Sale (66), to Clarke; Amory-Dexter; Fogg Art Museum, Harvard University, Gift of Mrs. Gordon Dexter (1942.180).

Bibliography: J. Prown, *John Singleton Copley* [exhibition catalogue], National Gallery of Art, Washington, D.C., The Metropolitan Museum of Art, New York, Museum of Fine Arts, Boston, 1965, 111, 141, fig. 113; J. Prown, *John Singleton* Copley, Cambridge, Mass., 1966, II, 327, 329, 402, 423, fig. 498.

In August 1787, Copley left London for Hanover to collect the portraits of the Hanoverian mercenaries who manned the garrison that had defeated the Spanish and French at Gibraltar on 13 September 1782. The portraits were later included in Copley's huge portrait-filled history picture, *The Siege of Gibraltar,* a commission he had won in competition with Benjamin West. The completed painting was executed over the years 1783–1791 and now hangs in the Guildhall Art Gallery, London.

In this splendid sketch, Copley portrays Colonel Ernst August von Hugo and Lieutenant Colonel von Schlepegrell in bold profile and strong colors against a light background of unfinished canvas. The vigorous brushwork and brilliant reds are among the most forceful aspects of the sketch. Copley evidently had the complete composition for *Gibraltar* in mind when he made this sketch, because the poses are the same as in the finished painting. The Fogg Museum also possesses two other oil sketches from this group of 1787: Colonel Gustav Friedrich von Dachenhausen (1942. 178) and Major August de la Motte (1942.179).

PH

John Singeton Copley

11 *Monmouth before James II Refusing to Give the Names of His Accomplices,* ca. 1782–1794

Pencil heightened with white chalk on blue paper, 13¾ x 11¼ inches

Signed lower left: J. S. Copley

Provenance: Probably Lyndhurst Library Sale, possibly (665), to Kempton; Victor Winthrop Newman; Fogg Art Museum, Harvard University, Purchase of the Louise E. Bettens Fund (1933.1).

Bibliography: J. Prown, *John Singleton Copley* [exhibition catalogue], National Gallery of Art, Washington, D.C., The Metropolitan Museum of Art, New York, Museum of Fine Arts, Boston, 1965, 122, 142, fig. 121; J. Prown, *John Singleton Copley,* Cambridge, Mass., 1966, II, 350, 444, fig. 603.

12 *Monmouth before James II Refusing to Give the Names of His Accomplices,* ca. 1782–1794

Sepia on canvas, 24¾ x 29⅝ inches

Provenance: Property of Lady DuCane, Christie, Feb. (?) 17, 1902, to Bregg; Baron Aberdare, 1908; Rt. Hon. Lord Aberdare and Other Collections Sale, Christie, June 3, 1932 (85); Fogg Art Museum, Harvard University, Gift of Mr. Copley Amory, Jr. (1957.225).

Bibliography: J. Prown, *John Singleton Copley* [exhibition catalogue], National Gallery of Art, Washington, D.C., The Metropolitan Museum of Art, New York, Museum of Fine Arts, Boston, 1965, 122, 142, fig. 120; J. Prown, *John Singleton Copley,* Cambridge, Mass., 1966, II, 350, 402, 444, fig. 605.

This drawing and sepia sketch are preliminary studies for Copley's unfinished painting, *Monmouth before James II,* of around 1795, in the Fogg Museum (1917.67). This large canvas, not exhibited, is closely related to Copley's painting of 1795, *Charles I Demanding in the House of Commons the Five Impeached Members,* now in the Boston Public Library. Prown says that the two were undoubtedly contemplated by Copley as pendant works, both depicting a seventeenth-century event in which a hero refused to betray his fellows to the king (Prown, *Copley,* II, 350).

Copley's procedure in creating a large history painting was to make a great quantity of preparatory studies. He began by drawing individual figures to determine the most effective poses and gestures. The drawing on blue paper is a study for the central figure of *Monmouth before James II,* and it agrees with the sepia study in all but the smallest particulars. He then combined the pencil studies in a series of intermediate sketches which led eventually to the refined sepia study. In the central and lower portions of the sepia study the drawn quadrants for transfer to the final canvas are visible.

PH

Benjamin West 1738–1820

13 *Self-Portrait,* 1793

Oil on panel, 36¼ x 29 inches

Inscribed lower left: By...and Dec 10 17...
Royal Academy   London

Provenance: Fogg Art Museum, Harvard University, Bequest of Grenville L. Winthrop (1943.163).

Bibliography: J. Galt, *The Life, Studies, and Works of Benjamin West, Esq.,* London, 1820, frontispiece; L. Cust, *History of the Society of Dilettanti,* London, 1898, 230-231; H. Jackson, *Benjamin West: His Life and Work,* Philadelphia, 1900, frontispiece; C. Harcourt-Smith, *The Society of Dilettanti: Its Regalia and Pictures,* London, 1932, 78-80, pl. 28.

The first American painter to enjoy an international reputation, Benjamin West became the historical painter to George III and succeeded Sir Joshua Reynolds as President of the Royal Academy. His studio in London became a center for American painters, many of whom reached their mature styles under his tutelage.

In 1792, West was elected to membership in the Society of Dilettanti and was requested to paint his self-portrait as an entrance gift. In a letter to the secretary of the Society, West states that he made two replicas of his self-portrait finished in 1793. Presumably the Fogg Museum self-portrait is one of them. The London portrait, now in the St. James Club, Piccadilly, is signed and dated, and the paper which West holds in his right hand bears an inscription "By Command-Decem' 10*th* 1768 Royal Academy of Arts London." December 10, 1768 was the date George III signed the charter establishing the Royal Academy. The sheet of paper in the Fogg Museum self-portrait bears this same inscription, although parts of it have been obscured due to abrasion.

West also became President of the Royal Academy in 1792, and on December 10, he delivered his first discourse to the students of the Academy. In it he traced the history of the development of the fine arts in Greece which he compared to the rapid maturation of the arts in England under the patronage of George III. He also stated that religion and the arts are inseparable. Included in the Fogg Museum self-portrait are a classical bust portrait of George III, a Bible and a History of England, direct references to the content of this speech.

PH

Benjamin West

14 *Fidelia and Spiranza,* 1784

Brown ink and watercolor on cream antique laid paper, 20 x 15 inches
Watermark: monogram PvL

Signed lower left: B. West 1784

Provenance: Fogg Art Museum, Harvard University, Bequest of Grenville L. Winthrop (1943.329).

Bibliography: *Connoisseur,* 50, 1918, fig. 63; *Grenville L. Winthrop, Retrospective for a Collector* [exhibition catalogue], Fogg Art Museum, Cambridge, Mass., 1969, no. 93.

West's drawing illustrates stanzas XII-XIV, Book 1, Canto X, of Edmund Spenser's intricate allegory of the moral virtues, *Faerie Queene.* This passage describes the encounter between Una and the Red Cross Knight and the daughters of Caelia. The elder, Fidelia:

... was arrayed all in lily white,
And in her right hand bore a cup of gold,
With wine and water fill'd up to the height,
In which a serpent did himself enfold,
That horror made to all that did behold;
But she no wit did change her constant mood:
And in her other hand she fast did hold
A book, that was both sign'd and seal'd
*   with blood;*
Wherein dark things were writ, hard to
*   be understood.*

Her younger sister, that Spiranza hight,
Was clad in blue that her beseemed well;
Not all so cheerful seemed she of sight,
As was her sister, whether dread did dwell
Or anguish in her heart, is hard to tell:
Upon her arm a silver anchor lay,
Whereon she leaned ever ....

It has been suggested that the composition follows West's painting (now lost) of the same subject which he exhibited at the Royal Academy in 1777 (*Grenville L. Winthrop, Retrospective for a Collector,* 132). Spenser's *Faerie Queene* offered West unparalleled opportunities to paint idealized human beings, and the poem inspired at least two other works: *Una and the Lion,* now in the Wadsworth Atheneum, and the *Cave of Despair,* mentioned in Galt's catalogue of West's works (J. Galt, *The Life, Studies, and Works of Benjamin West, Esq.,* London, 1820, 231).

PH

Charles Willson Peale   1741–1827

15   *George Washington,* 1784

Oil on canvas, 96 x 60 inches

Inscribed lower left: WASHINGTON

Provenance: Commissioned by Benjamin Harrison; Thomas Jefferson; the Duc de Mouchy, descendant of the Vicomte de Noailles, the brother-in-law of Lafayette; Fogg Art Museum, Harvard University, Bequest of Grenville L. Winthrop (1943.144).

Bibliography: J. Morgan and M. Fielding, *The Life Portraits of Washington,* Philadelphia, 1931, 36-37, no. 30; *Washington-Lafayette-Franklin* [exhibition catalogue], Fogg Art Museum, Cambridge, Mass., 1944, 7-10, fig. 6; C. Sellers, *Portraits and Miniatures by Charles Willson Peale,* Philadelphia, 1952, 236-237, no. 936, fig. 360.

Charles Willson Peale was perhaps the most diversely gifted of Philadelphia's colonial artists. With the exception of two years in West's studio (1767–1769), he had little formal training. A recorder of the leading Americans of his day, Peale's paintings have their greatest significance as historical documents.

This portrait of George Washington (1732–1799) is a replica of Peale's Annapolis portrait, but omits the figures of General Lafayette and Washington's aide-de-camp at Yorktown, Colonel Tench Tilghman. Washington stands in the conventional pose for portraits of men in high public esteem. An imposing physical presence, he appears rather like a Virginia gentleman instead of a stern commander. He stands before a tent beside a desk on which rests a document that reads: "York Virginia October 17, 1781/Articles of Capitulation . . ." In the distance, two officers display the colors of America and France, and between them the British colors are cased. Yorktown Heights completes the background.

The Harvard portrait was commissioned in 1783 by Governor Benjamin Harrison at the request of the Virginia Legislature (Morgan and Fielding, *Washington,* 36). Charles Coleman Sellers believes that the portrait was intended to serve as a model for a statue of Washington which was to be executed by the French sculptor, Houdon. Upon its completion in 1784, Peale sent the portrait to Paris. Houdon, however, rejected the plan to execute the statue in France from the painting. The portrait remained instead with Thomas Jefferson in Paris.

PH

WASHINGTON

16 *George Washington,* ca. 1775–1779

Ivory miniature; oval, 1⁹⁄₁₆ x 1⁵⁄₁₆ inches

Provenance: Mrs. Israel; inherited by Mrs. Hannah Faulkner Buck; her niece, Mrs. Hannah Jane Allen; her niece, Mrs. Mary Allen Fairfax to Edwin B. Holden, 1902; sale of Holden's collection 1910 (272) to W. B. Osgood Field; Harvard College Library, Gift of W. B. Osgood Field (Houghton Library MS AM 1375).

Bibliography: J. Morgan and M. Fielding, *The Life Portraits of Washington,* Philadelphia, 1931, 47-48, no. 60; *Washington-Lafayette-Franklin* [exhibition catalogue], Fogg Art Museum, Cambridge, Mass., 1944, 7; C. Sellers, *Portraits and Miniatures by Charles Willson Peale,* Philadelphia, 1952, 234, no. 929.

This miniature carries with it the apocryphal story that it was a gift from Washington to a certain Mrs. Israel in recognition of valuable information which she supplied concerning the British Army. Sellers regards it as a replica of Peale's full-length portrait of Washington, now in the Pennsylvania Academy of Fine Arts, Philadelphia; if so, the miniature must date from around 1779, the date Morgan and Fielding assign to the full-length Washington portrait.

The miniature portrait, still in its original pendant, has a bleached appearance that may be due in part to the customary tin backing, which reflects light back through the ivory and paint to give a quality of luminescence to the work.

PH

James Peale 1749–1831

17 *Portrait of a Young Girl,* ca. 1790–1800

Oil on canvas, 19½ x 17½ inches

Signed lower right: James Peale Pinx

Provenance: Fogg Art Museum, Harvard University, Bequest of Grenville L. Winthrop (1943.147).

The attribution of the *Portrait of a Young Girl* is problematic, because the signature is insufficient grounds for including the portrait in James Peale's oeuvre.

James Peale, the youngest brother of Charles Willson Peale, is best known as a miniaturist. The problem of distinguishing Peale from Peale is especially difficult, because individual styles within the Peale family of painters have not emerged precisely. Although the signature on the Fogg Museum portrait does not correspond with his customary signature, "I.P.," there are certain stylistic attributes that point to James Peale as the painter of this unidentified young girl. The stylized mouth with tucked-in corners is a consistent idiosyncrasy in Peale's work. His output of miniature paintings in the 1790's was prolific, and the *Portrait of a Young Girl,* with her large head, prominent eyes, and narrow shoulders, is closely reminiscent of his miniature of *Mrs. John McCluney* of 1794, now in the National Collection of Fine Arts, Smithsonian Institution (C. Elam, ed., *The Peale Family,* Detroit Institute of Arts, 1967, fig. 87). Finally, the *Portrait of a Young Girl* has an intimate, keepsake quality that suggests the work of the miniaturist, James Peale.

PH

18   *Jared Sparks,* ca. 1820–1825

Oil on canvas, 20⅛ x 15³⁄₁₆ inches

Provenance: Harvard University Portrait Collection, Bequest of Lizzie Sparks Pickering (H 244).

Bibliography: L. Huntsinger, *Harvard Portraits* (A. Burroughs, ed.), Cambridge, Mass., 1936, 128, fig. 129.

Rembrandt Peale was the second son of Charles Willson Peale. He studied eclectically in Europe during the first decade of the nineteenth century, initially under Benjamin West and then briefly in Paris, perhaps with Jacques Louis David and François Gerard.

The dominating impression of this portrait of Jared Sparks (1789–1866), biographer and president of Harvard, is Peale's association with the French school. In its formal qualities it exhibits an easily borne austerity without the typically American ingredient of frankness and concern for fine detail. The soft chiaroscuro and the clarity and fullness of form suggest French influence.

The youthful appearance of Sparks in this portrait suggests that it was painted long before 1838, when he became a professor at Harvard, but it is unclear whether it was painted in Baltimore or in Boston. Both Sparks and Peale were in Baltimore between 1819 and 1823; Sparks was the pastor of the First Independent Church (Unitarian), and Peale was the director of Peale's Museum and Gallery of Fine Arts. The occasion of Sparks' installation as pastor in 1819 is often referred to as "The Pentecost of American Unitarianism." Peale was a founding member of this church, and it is unlikely that the event or the man could have escaped his notice. Sparks moved to Boston in 1823, and since Peale's patronage also extended to Boston during the 1820's, it is possible that the portrait of Sparks was painted in Boston.

PH

John Trumbull 1756–1843

19 *Landscape with a Dead Tree,* ca. 1777–1783

Black and grey wash, 2⁷⁄₁₆ x 3⁷⁄₈ inches

Inscribed on the mat: John Trumbull 1783

Provenance: Fogg Art Museum, Harvard University, Bequest of Stephen Bleeker Luce (1962.108).

Bibliography: T. Sizer, *The Works of Colonel John Trumbull,* New Haven, 1967, 121.

Trumbull's *Autobiography* describes his initial efforts as a draughtsman in looking almost exclusively to book illustrations and to old engravings for inspiration. This small pen and wash drawing with Italianate details of style suggests that he also cast an interested eye to the work of Claude Lorrain. Compositionally, the drawing is very close to the illustrations after Claude in the *Liber Veritatis,* published in 1777, a work Trumbull may have known from his studies in the Harvard College Library. Especially reminiscent of Claude is the little parade of sheep and figures in the foreground, the tree which frames the right-hand side of the drawing, and the diagonal recession of space through the arched bridge into the atmospheric background. In his *Autobiography,* Trumbull does not mention Claude among his early sources, but the possibility that he had second-hand knowledge of his work cannot be overlooked. The drawing, executed in terms of Trumbull's own provincial experience, suggests a date earlier than 1783, the year traditionally assigned to it.

PH

John Trumbull

20 *Cardinal Guido Bentivoglio,* ca. 1777–1778

Oil on canvas, 29⁷⁄₁₆ x 24½ inches

Provenance: Harvard University Portrait Collection, Gift of John Trumbull, 1789 or 1791 (H 24).

Bibliography: *Letters and Papers of John Singleton Copley and Henry Pelham,* Massachusetts Historical Society, Boston, 1914, 240; L. Huntsinger, *Harvard Portraits* (A. Burroughs, ed.), Cambridge, Mass., 1936, 17-18; H. Foote, *John Smibert,* Cambridge, Mass., 1950; T. Sizer, ed., *The Autobiography of Colonel John Trumbull,* New Haven, 1953; W. Dunlap, *History of the Rise and Progress of the Arts of Design in the United States,* New York, 1965, 1, 18; T. Sizer, *The Works of Colonel John Trumbull,* New Haven, 1967, 20, fig. 5.

Trumbull was in Boston for some months in 1777–1778 between periods of active service in the Revolution. He hired the room John Smibert had once used as a painting studio. There he found copies of old master paintings that Smibert had painted and brought with him from Europe, among them Smibert's copy of Van Dyck's full-length portrait of Guido Bentivoglio. Trumbull's portrait is significant less for its artistic than its historical value. As a copy of Smibert's replica, it is a rare document which reveals how native artists, without benefit of European travel, learned to paint. In his *Autobiography* Trumbull mentions the copies he discovered in Smibert's room: "Mr. Copley was gone to Europe, and there remained in Boston no artist from whom I could gain oral instruction; but these copies supplied the place, and I made some progress." Trumbull also included in his *Autobiography* a list of drawings and paintings he made before his first trip to Europe in 1780. His Bentivoglio portrait is number thirty-seven: "Head of Cardinal Bentivoglio; copied from Smibert's/copy of Vandyck's celebrated portrait in the/Florence Gallery."

In the manuscript catalogue of his works owned by the Yale Library, Trumbull writes that he gave the portrait of Bentivoglio to Harvard College in 1789. According to Harvard records, the Corporation thanked Trumbull in 1791 for "a copy by the late Mr. Smibert of Boston from a portrait by Van Dyck of Cardinal Bentivoglio, a portrait highly celebrated" (College Book, VIII, 306). The discrepancy between the date of Trumbull's gift (1789) and

its receipt (1791) is unexplained, but on the basis of style we can be certain that the Bentivoglio portrait is by Trumbull.

To be sure, the Smibert portrait of Bentivoglio (now lost) was highly celebrated. By itself it constituted the first Boston school of art. Copley, Allston, and Trumbull all found in this one picture their first hints of a richer portrait tradition.

PH

John Trumbull

21 *John Adams,* ca. 1793

Oil on canvas, 30⁵⁄₁₆ x 24¼ inches

Provenance: Harvard University Portrait Collection, Gift of Andrew Craigie, 1794 (H 73).

Bibliography: L. Huntsinger, *Harvard Portraits* (A. Burroughs, ed.), Cambridge, Mass., 1936, 8; A. Oliver, *Portraits of John and Abigail Adams,* Cambridge, Mass., 1967, 66-68, fig. 28; T. Sizer, *The Works of Colonel John Trumbull,* New Haven, 1967, 18, fig. 1.

After scarcely two years of active service in the Revolutionary Army, Trumbull realized that the demands of war were far greater than the demand for painting, and that he could not pursue his work successfully in the colonies. He went to London to the studio of Benjamin West where he received instruction from 1780 to 1789. When he returned to America, Trumbull traveled along the eastern seaboard collecting portraits of revolutionary worthies, including Adams, for his projected series of history paintings.

Adams appears in a light olive-grey coat, partly unbuttoned. His ruddy complexion contrasts with the whiteness of his wig and the dark background. The portrait is an unusually conventional and superficial character study of the Vice President, a man whom Trumbull knew well.

Trumbull rarely signed and dated his works. This portrait was probably painted in Philadelphia in 1793 and is generally agreed to be a replica of a similar portrait of Adams in "Bedford House," Katonah, New York.

PH

22   *George Washington,* 1790

Oil on canvas, 30 x 25 inches

Signed lower left: E. Savage Pinx

Provenance: Harvard University Portrait Collection, Gift of Edward Savage, 1791 (H 49).

Bibliography: J. Morgan and M. Fielding, *The Life Portraits of Washington,* Philadelphia, 1931, no. 1, 180, fig. opp.; L. Huntsinger, *Harvard Portraits* (A. Burroughs, ed.), Cambridge, Mass., 1936, 143; *Washington-Lafayette-Franklin* [exhibition catalogue], Fogg Art Museum, Cambridge, Mass., 1944, 10.

This portrait of George Washington (1732–1799) is singularly interesting because it is a commissioned life-portrait painted in New York, 1789–1790. Washington appears in the Continental uniform with the gold eagle of the Order of the Cincinnati threaded through a buttonhole on his left coat lapel.

The circumstances attending the commission and execution of Harvard's only life-portrait of Washington are recorded in a letter to President Willard of Harvard and in Washington's diary. On 23 December 1789, Washington wrote to Willard that Savage " is now engaged in taking the portrait which you and the governors of the seminary over which you preside have expressed a desire for . . . ." Three extracts from Washington's diary refer to the painting: under the date of 21 December 1789, "Sat from ten to one o'clock for a Mr. Savage, to draw my portrait for the University of Cambridge, in the State of Massachusetts, at the request of the President and Governors of the said University." On 28 December, "Sat all the forenoon for Mr. Savage who is taking my portrait." And on 6 January 1790, "Sat from half after eight o'clock till ten for the portrait painter Mr. Savage, to finish the picture of me which he had begun for the University of Cambridge." Savage engraved a plate from the portrait and also painted a replica, now in the Adams Memorial Society of Quincy, Massachusetts.

PH

Gilbert Stuart   1755–1828

23   *George Washington,* ca. 1795–1796

Oil on canvas, 29 x 23¾ inches

Provenance: Fisher family, Philadelphia (?); George F. Tyler, 1921; Sydney F. Tyler; Harvard University Portrait Collection, Gift of Sydney F. Tyler, 1969 (H 631).

Bibliography: J. H. Morgan and M. Fielding, *The Life Portraits of Washington,* Philadelphia, 1931, 253.

Stuart was born in Rhode Island and spent his early years at Newport, where he first received instruction from the Scottish painter, Cosmo Alexander. He traveled to England and Scotland with Alexander but was forced to return home when Alexander died. Stuart returned to England on the eve of the Revolution and became an assistant to Benjamin West at the Royal Academy, where he matured to achieve prominence in London's fashionable art circles. He later moved to Ireland because of financial difficulties and returned to America in 1793 for the same reason. Preceding him was a reputation which placed him high in the ranks of Georgian portraitists.

One of Stuart's primary motives for returning was a desire to paint the President. He hoped to make his fortune by producing replicas of a portrait of Washington and by selling prints from an engraving after the painting.

Stuart painted Washington three times from life. The first was a bust portrait of the right side of Washington's face and has come to be known as the *Vaughan* type, after its first owner. Painted in Philadelphia in 1795, the canvas created a sensation when first exhibited; according to Stuart's list, dated 20 April 1795, he had orders for thirty-nine replicas of this portrait. Harvard's Vaughan portrait is documented as number six of the series in Morgan and Fielding, *Life Portraits of Washington.* It is alleged to have been purchased from the artist by Mr. Fisher of Philadelphia. As is common with a copy, the Harvard portrait is more constrained in style than the life portrait, but the work still remains an important and rare example of Stuart's first, most perceptive portrait of the President.

EAP

Gilbert Stuart

24 *Thomas Jefferson,* 1805

Grisaille on paper, 18⅜ x 18½ inches

Provenance: Mrs. T. Jefferson Newbold; Fogg Art Museum, Harvard University, Given in memory of Thomas Jefferson Newbold, Harvard Class of 1912, by Mrs. T. Jefferson Newbold and Family (1960.156).

Bibliography: L. Park, *Gilbert Stuart,* New York, 1926, I, 440; J. Prown, *Harvard Alumni Bulletin,* Sept. 24, 1960, 15.

This portrait of Jefferson was completed in the spring of 1805 and is unique in the context of Stuart's oeuvre. Prown notes that Jefferson sat for Stuart three times for portraits, and that on the occasion of this, the third, Jefferson requested Stuart to paint him "à l'antique." The resulting portrait medallion, which is the only one of its kind known by the artist, apparently pleased Jefferson, for it hung in the White House until 1809, when he removed it to Monticello. The work casts an informative light upon Jefferson's own tastes and reveals yet another dimension of his preference for antique models as a viable source for the contemporary arts of America.

EAP

Gilbert Stuart

25 *Mrs. Israel Thorndike, Jr.,* ca. 1811

Oil on panel, 33 x 26½ inches

Inscribed on reverse: Belonging to—Thorndike

Provenance: Thorndike family; Mrs. Earl Morse; Harvard University Portrait Collection, Gift of Mrs. Earl Morse, 1954 (H 555).

Bibliography: L. Park, *Gilbert Stuart,* New York, 1926, II, 751.

Mrs. Israel Thorndike, Jr. (1793–1819), was the daughter-in-law of Colonel Israel Thorndike of Beverly and Boston. As captain of the privateer *Warren,* he made several captures during the Revolution, and when peace was declared he turned his attention to commerce with China and East India. Colonel Thorndike was elected to the Massachusetts convention that ratified the Constitution. He settled in Boston in 1810 and in 1818 purchased the library of C. D. Ebeling of Hamburg, Germany, a collection of 10,000 maps and over 3,200 books, which he subsequently gave to Harvard. Mrs. Thorndike's parents were Harrison Gray Otis and Sally Foster.

Stuart has represented the seemingly apprehensive figure against billowing red baroque curtains, and she is painted in the thin style which the artist favored after his return to America in 1793. Stuart was more comfortable when confronted by a statesman or politician than he was with a female, and he was not cordially disposed to such commissions. Certain visual evidence in the portrait confirms the fact that he probably hurried with this work; Mrs. Thorndike's hair is very thinly brushed, and the right arm of the chair bends away, contradicting the logic of perspective. These, however, are only minor idiosyncrasies in what is one of the artist's more effective portraits.

EAP

Gilbert Stuart

26 *John Quincy Adams,* ca. 1825–1830

Oil on canvas, 94⅞ x 59⅞ inches

Signed and dated lower left: Stuart 1825 T.S. 1830

Provenance: Harvard University Portrait Collection, Bequest of Ward Nicholas Boylston, 1828 (H 187).

Bibliography: H. Adams, letter to A. Pope dated 16 June 1948, unpublished, Fogg Art Museum, Harvard University; A. Oliver, *Portraits of John Quincy Adams and His Wife,* Cambridge, Mass., 1970, 122-123; L. Park, *Gilbert Stuart,* New York, 1926, I, 95-96; M. Sadik, *The Life Portraits of John Quincy Adams* [exhibition catalogue], Smithsonian Institution, Washington, D. C., 1970, 15.

Stuart began this full-length portrait as a commission for Ward Nicholas Boylston in 1825. According to Park, he proceeded only as far as copying the head, which he modeled after the bust portrait of Adams he had painted in 1818. Old age or perhaps the artist's notorious indifference toward certain commissions prevented completion of the canvas, and it remained in Stuart's studio until his death. Sadik notes that the matter was complicated by a dispute over costume between Adams, who wanted to appear in "plain American dress," and Boylston, who wished him to be shown in the formal attire Adams had worn at the Court of St. James. Both Stuart and Boylston died in 1828 before artist, patron, and sitter could agree, and in 1829 Thomas Sully was commissioned to complete the canvas.

Adams had apparently stipulated to Stuart that his lyre and eagle seal should appear in the portrait, and Sully complied with these instructions as well as those requesting the artist to portray him in everyday dress. The seal is shown hanging from the fob and is an accurate reproduction, according to Henry Adams.

EAP

Benjamin Greenleaf   1786–1864

27 *Cotton Tufts,* 1804

Oil on canvas, 28⅞ x 22½ inches

Signed and dated on the back: Hon Cotton Tufts M.D. A.A.L./M.M.S. Drawn in the 73rd year of his life 1804/By Benjamin Greenleaf.

Provenance: Dr. Cotton Tufts; Dr. William T. Brigham; Boston Medical Library in the Countway Library of Medicine, Harvard Medical School, Gift of Dr. William T. Brigham, 1878.

Bibliography: J. Thacher, *American Medical Biography,* II, Boston, 1828, 149-152; T. F. Harrington, *The Harvard Medical School, a History, Narrative, and Documentary, 1782–1905,* I, New York and Chicago, 1905, 45-46; J. Lipman, "Benjamin Greenleaf, New England Limner," *Antiques,* 52, 1947, 195-197; L. H. Butterfield, ed., "Descriptive List of Illustrations," *Adams Family Correspondence,* II, New York, 1964, xi; N. F. Little, *Country Art in New England, 1790–1840,* Sturbridge, Mass., 1964, 29.

Dr. Cotton Tufts (1732–1815), who practiced medicine in Weymouth, Massachusetts, was a chief organizer and for eight years president of the Massachusetts Medical Society. A prominent figure in the American Revolution, he drafted Weymouth's document of opposition to the Stamp Act and later served in the Massachusetts Senate. Nicknamed "Old Trusty" by the Adams family, he was the intermediary for the love letters of John and Abigail and managed their property and business interests during their absences. Tufts was a charter member of the American Academy of Arts and Sciences.

The artist, Benjamin Greenleaf, taught high school mathematics and wrote textbooks on the subject. He financed his college education by painting portraits, chiefly on glass. That of Tufts is Greenleaf's earliest recorded effort and his only known portrait on canvas. The work is primitive in its abrupt perspective, flatness of features and dress, and absence of shaded modeling. These qualities reflect a lack of formal artistic training, as well as Greenleaf's upbringing without exposure to the artistic culture of the day. In style the Tufts portrait resembles far more the native primitive painting of late seventeenth- and early eighteenth-century New England than works by Greenleaf's own contemporaries such as Harding and Frothingham. Nevertheless, this likeness is a convincing, forthright characterization of Cotton Tufts.

KDR

John Vanderlyn   1775–1852

28   *Portrait of Governor Elbridge Gerry,* 1798

Black chalk on buff paper, 8 x 6½ inches

Inscribed on the back: taken at Paris the beginning of July 1798 by Mr. Vanderlyn, a young gentleman of New York

Provenance: Governor Elbridge Gerry; his daughter, Emily L. Gerry; Elbridge Gerry Greene, Boston; Vose Galleries, Boston; Fogg Art Museum, Harvard University, Purchase of the Louise E. Bettens Fund (1943.1817).

Bibliography: K. Lindsay, *The Works of John Vanderlyn* [exhibition catalogue], Binghamton, New York, 1970, 127.

29   *Portrait of Mahlon Dickerson,* ca. 1820

Oil on canvas, 36 x 28½ inches

Provenance: Harvard Law School Collection.

Bibliography: R. G. Stewart, *A Nineteenth Century Gallery of Distinguished Americans* [exhibition catalogue], Washington, D.C., 1969, 2-4.

Vanderlyn was one of the several ambitious American painters who at the turn of the nineteenth century fought to change, or elevate, American taste. Born in Kingston, New York, he studied under Archibald Robertson and for a few months with Gilbert Stuart before going to Paris in 1796 with his patron, Aaron Burr. He returned to New York in 1801 for a brief period but went back to Europe where he remained for the next twelve years. Vanderlyn produced his best work abroad, and when he finally returned to America he desired, as did Allston, Morse, and others, to make his reputation as a history painter. The attitude of this country, however, was not congenial toward this mode of painting, and Vanderlyn found it necessary to rely on portraiture as his primary means of support. Harvard possesses two superb portraits by him from his early and middle period.

The small portrait sketch of Elbridge Gerry (1744–1814) was completed when Vanderlyn was a student in Paris and Mr. Gerry was a diplomat in France. Aaron Burr probably arranged the sitting with Mr. Gerry.

Lindsay reproduces excerpts from a letter of 13 July 1798 that Vanderlyn wrote to his brother. In it he mentioned using black chalk for a "few little portraits." He went on to say: "I have made Mr. Gerry a present of his likeness (small) which he takes home with him.

Already there is one of my doing in Boston (in or on the way at least) as you can see I ran the chance of being known before I am seen."

The drawing was engraved by John R. Smith in 1811 and by J. B. Longacre (published as a frontispiece in James T. Austin, *The Life of Elbridge Gerry,* Boston, 1828). Four oil copies exist, one by Jocelyn.

This portrait shows the first influences of French portraiture and the school of David and breaks with the tradition of English Georgian portraiture on which American painters, Stuart for instance, had formed their styles. Broadly and evenly lighted, the portrait does not idealize the sitter but communicates his personality directly.

Vanderlyn's approach to the portrait as an art form stayed close to the norm established by his early portrait of Mr. Gerry, as this later painting of Mahlon Dickerson attests. This Harvard portrait was engraved by G. Parker for inclusion in the publication of *The National Portrait Gallery of Distinguished Americans,* and it is illustrated in volume III, page 99, according to Stewart. Mahlon Dickerson (1770–1853) was prominent in early American politics, first as a member of the New Jersey Supreme Court (1812–1815), then as Governor of New Jersey (1815–1817), and later as Senator (1817–1833). His oil portrait shows the influence of French neoclassical portraiture. The rich, brown background and clearly lighted head are derived from David.

EAP

Washington Allston   1779–1843

30   *Diana in the Chase,* 1805

Oil on canvas, 64¾ x 95½ inches

Provenance: Mrs. Edward Moore; Fogg Art Museum, Harvard University, Gift of Mrs. Edward Moore (1956.62).

Bibliography: E. P. Richardson, *Washington Allston,* New York, 1948, 69; B. Rowland, "Diana in the Chase by Washington Allston," *Fogg Art Museum Annual Report,* 1955–1956, Cambridge, Mass., 48-49.

Washington Allston, born in South Carolina, was raised in an atmosphere unaffected by the coldly objective morality of New England, a fact which would have great significance in determining the direction of his mature painting. Introduced to the rudiments of painting and draughtsmanship by Samuel King during his school days in Newport, Allston did not make a commitment to painting as a profession until his final years at Harvard. After his graduation he departed in 1801 for Europe, where he worked under the guidance of Benjamin West at the Royal Academy in London prior to traveling extensively on the continent.

Diana was painted in 1805 when Allston was in Rome with Samuel Coleridge and Washington Irving; it is one of the first large-scale romantic landscapes produced by this artist, who was to become the quintessential proponent of romantic painting in America. Based on innumerable sketches of trees and foliage, including views of Mount Pilatus, the composition shows the influence of Venetian painting and is constructed on the formula of Claude Lorrain, with a dark, enframing foreground leading into a luminous middle distance. Allston's primary concern was to elevate landscape to the level of the grandiose, and this perhaps explains the almost incidental presence of small, generalized figures from ancient mythology, which transform a pure landscape into a history painting and make the work conform to the classical tradition dominating European academic painting at that time.

Coleridge mentioned the "picturesque," "coloristic" qualities of this "Swiss landskip" and spoke with delight of the tree which appears at the left of the composition; "the divine, semi-transparent, grey-green light on the highest part of the trunk of this smoke tree . . . seen through its vapor cloud of foliage."

EAP

Washington Allston

31 *Female Head,* ca. 1815

Charcoal and chalk on blue paper, 6 x 4 inches

Provenance: Fogg Art Museum, Harvard University, Washington Allston Trust (8-1955.15).

32 *Jason Returning to Demand His Father's Kingdom,* ca. 1807–1808

Black crayon on paper mounted on canvas, 34¾ x 44 inches

Provenance: Fogg Art Museum, Harvard University, Washington Allston Trust (98.1942).

Bibliography: W. Gerdts, "Washington Allston and the German Romantic Classicists in Rome," *The Art Quarterly,* 32, 1969, 191; E. P. Richardson, *Washington Allston,* New York, 1948, 81-83.

Allston's European trip plunged him into an experience of art dominated by a neoclassicism which looked to the antique and the Renaissance for its own inspiration. The small chalk drawing of a young girl probably dates from Allston's first European period. Its classical elegance and smooth, idealized form reflect the same reverence for the antique world as that maintained by Benjamin West and the French neoclassic masters, whose work Allston used as a model for his own. This stylized female type appears in Allston's art as early as 1805 and can be traced throughout his oeuvre. Allston, consistent with the English and French academicians, standardized this image into a virtual formula without really developing it much beyond its present state, a fact which makes the drawing difficult to date precisely.

A more specific antecedent is his study for *Jason.* This interesting work preceded a huge (14 x 20 feet) unfinished canvas of the same subject which was inspired by Allston's experience of Renaissance painting, specifically Raphael, while he was in Rome. Coleridge says that Allston worked eighteen months on the composition, which he was forced to leave in England on his departure from Europe. It was not until 1815 that he saw it again, but by that time he had lost interest not only in the picture but in classical antiquity as a subject. "After that experiment I never tried another classic subject," he said long after. "The whole sympathy of my mind is with the Gothic and Romantic forms of art."

The composition has behind it many diverse influences, beginning with Raphael and Poussin and terminating with the more contemporary influences of David and the French neoclassic painters as well as the German romantic classicists. Easily the most classical of Allston's pictures, it stands practically isolated in his oeuvre.

EAP

Washington Allston

33 *Ship in a Squall,* before 1837

Chalk drawing on brown-primed canvas, 48⅛ x 60 inches

Provenance: Fogg Art Museum, Harvard University, Washington Allston Trust (119.1942).

Bibliography: T. Leavitt, "Permanent Loans from the Washington Allston Trust," *Fogg Art Museum Annual Report, 1954–1955,* Cambridge, Mass., 14; E. P. Richardson, *Washington Allston,* New York, 1948, 150-152.

This large chalk drawing was discovered in the artist's studio after his death. It is a preparatory study for what was conceived as a major seascape, but Allston abandoned the work in its first stage. For Allston this practice was not unusual; he would often work on his pictures in phases, first marking out his initial conception in chalk, then fixing the design with oil before completing the laborious process of glazing. Throughout the latter part of his life, Allston had great difficulty with the problem of finishing his canvases, however, and much of his time was spent attempting to complete *Belshazzar's Feast.* It is possible that *Ship in a Squall* was abandoned in favor of this larger work, but it could have also succumbed to Allston's very fragile and delicate temperament.

This study has a precedent in an earlier work entitled *Rising of a Thunderstorm at Sea,* in the collection of the Museum of Fine Arts, Boston, dated 1805; but in this later work the threatening imminence of the storm is intimated rather than described. Allston has also established a mood of mystery, even possible terror, by emphasizing the vastness and emptiness of the space, of nature dominant. It is possible that Allston purposely allowed the work to stand complete as a drawing, for its freshness and immediacy would not have projected with the same force had the picture been completed with oil glazes. Allston's glazing process was more comfortably suited to subjects taken from antiquity which could be studied and worked; as it is, *Ship in a Squall* assumes a position unique in the artist's oeuvre and is representative of his spontaneous, expansive side.

EAP

Alvan Fisher 1792–1863

34 *View of Harvard Yard,* ca. 1821

Pen and ink on white paper, 10 x 15 inches

Provenance: Houghton Library, Harvard University (48m-267).

Bibliography: H. V. Bail, *Views of Harvard,* Cambridge, Mass., 1949, 148-162.

35 *Landscape (Merrimac River?),* ca. 1830

Oil on canvas, 26¼ x 36 inches

Provenance: Harvard Graduate School of Business Administration.

Fisher was a pioneer of American genre and landscape painting. He was born in Needham, Massachusetts, and began painting sometime around 1812, receiving instruction from John Ritto Penniman. He wrote to William Dunlap: "In 1814 I commenced *being* an artist, by painting portraits at a cheap rate. This I pursued until 1815. I then began painting a species of pictures which had not been practiced much, if any, in this country, viz: barnyard scenes and scenes belonging to rural life . . . " (W. Dunlap, *History of the Rise of the Arts of Design in the United States,* New York, 1834, III, 32-34).

His view of Harvard Yard, probably completed in 1821, served as the study for an engraving; this is indicated by the fact that it is measured off for copying. This engraving, and a companion view which represents Harvard Yard from the northeast, were published on 1 May 1823. Fisher also painted two views of the Yard in oil which now hang in the president's office. This study provided the source for both the engraving and the oil of the south view.

Fisher traveled to England, France, Switzerland, and Italy and studied in Paris. His river landscape shows the influence of European painting in its broad, sweeping scale. The shattered tree stump in one corner of the canvas appears often in the pictures of Thomas Cole, but it is difficult to say whether Fisher knew Cole's work. The inclusion in this picture of what appears to be long factory or mill structures indicates that the work was executed sometime after the advent of industrialism in this country. The conflict between pure landscape and industrialism, or civilization, was to be a major theme of early American landscape painting. The landscape represented could be a view of the early mills that were constructed near Boston or Lowell on the Merrimac River.

EAP

Samuel F. B. Morse   1791–1872

36   *Mrs. Jedidiah Morse,* ca. 1820

Oil on panel, 10 x 8 inches

Provenance: Grenville L. Winthrop; Fogg Art Museum, Harvard University, Bequest of Grenville L. Winthrop (1943.143).

After graduating from Yale, Morse departed for England with his master, Washington Allston. He returned to the United States in 1815 after four years of European study, hopeful of establishing himself as a painter of classical and literary themes. Morse regarded portrait painting as demeaning, and in 1815 remarked in a letter: "I do not speak of portrait-painters; had I no higher thoughts than being a first-rate portrait-painter, I would have chosen a far different profession. My ambition is to be among those who shall revive the splendour of the fifteenth century" (H. B. Wehle, *Samuel F. B. Morse: American Painter,* New York, 1932, 7).

His ambitions went unfulfilled, and soon after his return from Europe he set out to paint portraits, first in New England (1816–1817), then in Charleston, South Carolina (1818–1821) and in New Haven (1821-1823), before finally opening a New York studio.

Many of these early portraits are small, cabinet-sized works of which *Mrs. Jedidiah Morse* is a typical example. Several members of his family sat for Morse during these early years when patronage was slow, and on more than one occasion he painted a portrait of his mother. This small picture is representative of his early work, so filled with difficulties and frustrations.

EAP

Henry Inman   1801–1846

37   *Levi Woodbury,* 1826

Oil on canvas, 9¾ x 7¾ inches

Inscribed on back: Gov. Levi Woodbury, Inman, 1826

Provenance: Harvard Law School Collection.

Henry Inman painted a variety of subjects including full portraits, miniatures, genre, and landscape. He was born in Utica, New York, and in 1814 commenced a seven-year apprenticeship under J. W. Jarvis in New York City. In the year this picture was painted, Inman was deeply involved in the founding of the National Academy of Design, of which he was elected the first vice president in 1827.

This small portrait belongs to the same tradition of cabinet protraiture represented elsewhere in the exhibition in the work of George Linen and S. F. B. Morse. There is a conflict between Mr. Woodbury's biography and his title as described by Inman on the reverse of the portrait. Levi Woodbury was Governor of New Hampshire in 1823. From 1825 to 1831 he served as U. S. Senator and later became the nation's Secretary of the Treasury before receiving an appointment to the Supreme Court. At the time of this painting, then, Mr. Woodbury was a Senator; Inman's signature and inscription must have been added sometime after the picture was completed.

EAP

Charles Bird King 1785–1862

38 *Hoo-wan-ne-ka, Little Elk, Winnebago Chief,*
ca. 1821

Oil on panel, 24¾ x 20¾ inches

Provenance: David Ives Bushnell, Jr.; Peabody
Museum, Harvard University, Bushnell Collection (41-72-10/417).

Charles Bird King was a native of Newport,
Rhode Island, and was introduced to painting
in that city by Samuel King. He later studied
under Edward Savage in New York City and
from 1805–1812 with Benjamin West at the
Royal Academy in London. King finally settled
in Washington, D. C., where he established a
reputation as a painter of the Indian visitors
to the nation's capital.

King began his series of Indian portraits in
1821 when a delegation of sixteen chieftans
from the Kansa, Pawnee, and other plains
tribes visited Washington and met President
James Monroe. According to J. C. Ewers
(*Artists of the Old West,* New York, 1965, 51),
Thomas L. McKenny, Superintendent of Indian
Trade from 1816 to 1822, induced King to paint
his first Indian portraits and later, as head of
the Bureau of Indian Affairs, McKenny was
instrumental in founding the National Indian
Portrait Gallery. In 1858 this gallery, com-
prising 147 works, many by King, was transferred to the Smithsonian Institution where on
15 January 1865 fire destroyed all but a few
pictures. It is unknown whether this picture
is a survivor of the Smithsonian fire or a replica painted after the fact; the possibility exists that it was simply retained by the artist
after painting, for it is illustrated in James
Hall, *History of the Indian Tribes of North
America,* a monumental three-volume study
which was published in Philadelphia from 1836
to 1844. A plate from this work is in the Bushnell Collection in the Peabody Museum at
Harvard.

In this portrait, as in many others by King,
the chief wears a peace medal, a round medallion of a type first struck in 1801 during the
term of Jefferson, bearing his likeness and
later those of each successive president; the
reverse side contains a symbol of peace (M.
Rosen, *The Redwood Library Collection: North
American Indian Portraits by Charles Bird
King,* Parke Bernet, New York, 1970, VII). Little Elk appears to wear the Monroe medal,
which suggests that he was one of the first
chiefs to be painted by King.

EAP

Charles Bird King

39 *The Anatomy of Art Appreciation* (also called
The Vanity of the Artist's Dream), 1830

Oil on canvas, 35¼ x 29½ inches

Signed and dated lower center: C. B. King 1839

Provenance: Grenville L. Winthrop; Fogg Art
Museum, Harvard University, Bequest of
Grenville L. Winthrop (1942.193).

Bibliography: W. H. Gerdts and R. Burke,
American Still Life Painting, New York, 1971,
52-53.

King was known primarily for his Indian portraits, but he also painted at least two satiric
still lifes which comment on the ironic plight
of an artist in America. This picture, the later
of the two, is more complex in its choice and
arrangement of objects and subtler in written
text. One of the central passages is inscribed
in the open book above the half loaf of bread,
and reads:

*The exhibition of a Catskin in Philadelphia
    produced
Twelve Hundred Dollars, totally eclipsing
    its rival,
the splendid portrait of West
    by Sir T. Lawrence, the
latter we regret did not produce enough
    to pay its expenses.
Oh: Athens of America!*

The Harvard picture and King's earlier satire,
The Poor Artist's Cupboard, Corcoran Gallery
of Art, Washington, are of particular interest
since they, along with Raphaelle Peale's pictures, anticipate the later development of
trompe-l'oeil painting which flourished in
America during the 1880's and 1890's. It is possible that King was inspired in these efforts by
examples of European trompe-l'oeil painting
which he saw in London (W. Born, "Notes on
Still Life Painting in America," *Antiques,* Sept.
1945, 158-160). They might also be "vanitas"
pictures in reverse, as W. Gerdts and R. Burke
have suggested. Instead of drawing a contrast
between worldly wealth and mortality, they
wryly contrast an ideal of good living with
the hard realities of the artist's life.

EAP

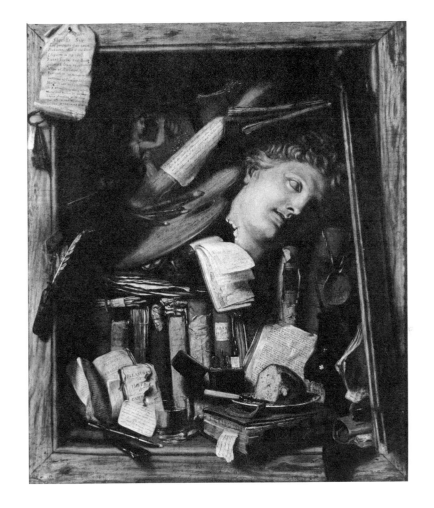

John James Audubon 1785–1851

40 *Blackcock,* 1827

Oil on canvas, 46¾ x 71¼ inches

Signed and dated lower right: J. J. Audubon, Edinburgh 1827

Provenance: John E. Thayer to Museum of Comparative Zoology, Harvard University; Fogg Art Museum, Harvard University (1964.147).

41 *Wild Turkey Cock and Hen and Nine Chicks,* 1827

Oil on canvas, 46¾ x 71¼ inches

Signed and dated lower right: J. J. Audubon, Edinburgh 1827

Provenance: John E. Thayer to Museum of Comparative Zoology, Harvard University; Fogg Art Museum, Harvard University (1964.146).

Bibliography: E. H. Dwight, "Audubon's Oils," *Art in America,* 51, 1963, 77-79.

Audubon was born in Haiti, but spent his early life in France where he received some formal instruction in the atelier of Jacques Louis David. After moving to the United States, he was taught how to paint in oils in 1820 by an itinerant painter named John Stein and in 1822 took some lessons from Thomas Sully.

From 1820 until his death, Audubon was occupied by studying and painting birds and mam-

mals, and in 1826, after years of concentrated application, he sailed for England to procure an engraver and solicit subscriptions for his monumental portfolio, *Birds of America*. Up to this time he had concentrated his effort in the medium of watercolor, but during his stay in London, and later in Edinburgh, Audubon painted oil copies of a few of his early watercolors, some of which he gave to friends or sold to help finance his portfolio. Both of these large compositions were painted in Scotland, and *Blackcock* is supposed to have been exhibited at the Royal Institution in England. His *Wild Turkey Cock* is perhaps more well known, for it appeared as the first plate in *Birds of America* and has been widely reproduced.

Audubon's tight, linear style was influenced by the draughtsmanly tradition of David and French academic art and was well suited to aquatint, for it allowed the artist to adhere with almost scientific precision to the appearances presented by the birds and mammals he so assiduously studied. Working in oil in a large format occupied by many images presented some problems for Audubon, and although his compositions here are not fully unified, they exhibit, nevertheless, a distinct strength, particularly the single images of the birds.

EAP

Thomas Sully 1783–1872

42 *John McAllister, Jr.,* 1830–1831

Oil on canvas, 25 x 30 inches

Inscribed on back: John McAllister, Jr. 1831, aged 45 years. T S 1831

Provenance: Grenville L. Winthrop; Fogg Art Museum, Harvard University, Bequest of Grenville L. Winthrop (1943.157).

43 *Mrs. John McAllister, Jr.,* 1830–1831

Oil on canvas, 25 x 30 inches

Inscribed on the back: (Eliza) McAllister 1831 T S 1831

Provenance: Grenville L. Winthrop; Fogg Art Museum, Harvard University, Bequest of Grenville L. Winthrop (1943.158).

Bibliography: C. H. Hart, ed., *A Register of Portraits by Thomas Sully*, Philadelphia, 1908, 109; E. Biddle and M. Fielding, *The Life and Works of Thomas Sully*, Philadelphia, 1921, 216-217.

Thomas Sully was born in England, but in 1792 his family emigrated to Charleston, South Carolina. He took painting lessons from his brother-in-law, Jean Belzens, and his brother, Lawrence. After studying with Benjamin West in London in 1809–1810, he settled in Philadelphia and became the city's leading portraitist.

A Philadelphia optician, John McAllister, Jr., was a well-known antiquary and collector of art and is alleged to have been, at the time of his death, the oldest graduate of the University of Pennsylvania. According to Sully's notes, this portrait was begun on 16 December 1830 and finished on 22 January 1831, and that of Mrs. McAllister begun on 13 December 1830 and completed on 12 January 1831.

Occasionally criticized for lack of strength in his portraits, Sully more than made up for this by his singular ability to capture the fleeting effects of expression and mood in a sitter's face. The portrait of Mrs. McAllister is a marvelously revealing document attesting to the artist's sensitive insight. It is perhaps more psychologically revealing and compelling than that of her husband. The two together combine to form a testament to the ability of this early master and define the middle-class patronage which made up the corpus of the artist's work at this period in his life.

EAP

Thomas Cole 1801–1848

44 *House, Mt. Desert, Maine,* ca. 1844

Oil on canvas, 17½ x 23½ inches

Provenance: Edward Charles Pickering; Fogg Art Museum, Harvard University, Bequest of Edward Charles Pickering, 1919 (1956.222).

In 1818 Thomas Cole emigrated to America with his family from Lancashire, England. He began portrait painting in 1822 and traveled through many small Ohio towns seeking patronage. Gradually, however, he developed an interest in landscape painting and moved to Philadelphia, where he studied occasionally at the Pennsylvania Academy of Fine Arts. In 1825 Cole moved to New York and made his first sketching trip up the Hudson River; the resulting landscapes brought him immediate fame and gave birth to the so-called Hudson River School of landscape painters. The following year he was elected to the National Academy and began to summer in Catskill, New York, where he permanently settled in 1836.

Cole was the first American painter to conceptualize American landscape at the romantic and grandiose level of European history painting. Preceding this small landscape are such monumental pieces as the *Voyage of Life* and his *Course of Empire series.* This much less pretentious landscape was painted in 1844 when Cole made a trip to Mt. Desert Island, Maine, with his pupil, Frederic E. Church and a friend, Henry C. Pratt. Cole described this scene in a letter to his wife: "We lost our road too, and came to a romantic place near a mountain gorge, with a deserted house and a piece of meadow" (L. L. Noble, *The Life and Works of Thomas Cole,* Cambridge, Mass., 1964, 270). The shattered tree trunk in the left corner of the canvas is a standard design element incorporated in many of his pictures. In this work it introduces the viewer to a quiet, contemplative scene which shows the inroads of civilization and settlement being slowly eroded by the primal forces of nature.

EAP

George Linen 1802–1888

45 *Portrait of James Gallatin,* ca. 1840

Oil on panel, 6⅞ x 5¾ inches

Provenance: Grenville L. Winthrop; Fogg Art Museum, Harvard University, Bequest of Grenville L. Winthrop (1943.134).

Born in Scotland, Linen studied at the Royal Scottish Academy in Edinburgh. He came to America in 1834 and settled permanently in New York in 1843, where he painted portraits of a small size. This diminutive portrait of James Gallatin is a superb example from his hand. James was the son of Albert Gallatin, eminent statesman, leader of the Republican Party and Secretary of the Treasury from 1801 to 1813. Before photography became the popular means of capturing a likeness on a small and intimate scale, miniature painting fulfilled that function. This small portrait is not in the purest definition a miniature painting, for it is done on panel and not on ivory backed with tin, but its size conforms to that tradition of keepsake art.

EAP

William Sidney Mount   1807–1868

46 *Portrait of a Lady,* 1842

Pencil on white paper, 9¾ x 7¹¹⁄₁₆ inches

Signed and dated lower right: Wm. S. Mount, Del., Jan. 1842

Provenance: Fogg Art Museum, Harvard University, Purchase of the Louise E. Bettens Fund (1941.18).

Mount was born in the village of Setauket, Long Island, and developed into America's first major genre painter, commonly employing themes suggested by the rural environment of his birthplace. His work can be interpreted as an expression of Jacksonian democracy which, along with the landscape painting of the Hudson River School painters, radiates a sense of optimism and self-confidence.

By 1824 he was in New York working in his brother's sign-painting shop, visiting the American Academy galleries, and studying occasionally with Henry Inman. He began his career painting portraits, but during the thirties and forties, as his style matured, he showed a marked preference for genre subjects. Rural America appealed to Mount, and although he was presented with a number of opportunities to go abroad, he preferred the quiet of Long Island.

This elegant portrait drawing belongs to a group of works similar in style which he produced in 1841–1842. They reveal a profound influence of nineteenth-century French academic portraiture and suggest an immediate source in the precise draughtsmanship of Ingres. Mount was undoubtedly familiar with French engravings, since many of his own works were lithographed in Paris by Goupil, Vilbert and Company, a firm which even offered to finance a trip abroad for him and probably supplied the artist with examples of contemporary French achievements. His use of *Del.* (he drew it) following his signature might have been a conscious affectation to advertise his knowledge of European sources.

EAP

George Caleb Bingham 1811–1879

47 *Concealed Enemy,* 1845

Oil on canvas, 28½ x 35½ inches

Provenance: Purchased from the artist by the American Art Union, New York, December 8, 1845, and awarded by them to James A. Hutchison, Pittsburgh, Pa., on December 19, 1845; David Ives Bushnell, Jr.; Peabody Museum, Harvard University, Bushnell Collection (41-72-10/28).

Bibliography: J. F. McDermott, *George Caleb Bingham,* Norman, Oklahoma, 1959, 50, 53, 190, 411; E. M. Bloch, *George Caleb Bingham,* Berkeley, 1967, I, 110-111.

Bingham is known primarily for the genre and political pictures whose good-natured humor gave visual credibility to a way of life that would be further popularized a generation later in the writings of Mark Twain. Born in Virginia, Bingham moved with his family to Missouri in 1819, and it was as a Missouri River painter and political satirist that he made his reputation. He studied art at the Pennsylvania Academy in 1837 and at the Düsseldorf School in Germany from 1856 to 1859.

The Indian theme, which was highly popular during the first half of the nineteenth century, never became central to Bingham's work. He was apparently more interested in the buoyant vitality of the river life and the excitement which attended local political elections. Bingham never came into close association with tribal life and did not manifest an interest in developing the Indian theme on the level of romantic fiction.

EAP

George Catlin 1796–1872

48 *Wan-ee-ton,* 1868

Oil on paper, 16½ x 11¾ inches

Inscribed on back: Wan-ee-ton. Chief of the Susseton Ban of Sioux. A very distinguished man. Geo. Catlin, p. 1868

Provenance: The Smithsonian Institution, Washington, D. C., to David Ives Bushnell, Jr., in exchange for a wampum necklace and a wristlet, August 1918; Peabody Museum, Harvard University, Bushnell Collection (41-72-10/63).

Catlin was the first American artist to concern himself with the ethnology of the American Plains Indian. "I have, for many years past, contemplated the noble races of red men who are now spread over these trackless forests and boundless prairies, melting away at the approach of civilization. Their rights invaded, their morals corrupted, their lands wrested from them, their customs changed, and therefore lost to the world . . . I have flown to their rescue — not of their lives or of their race (for they are 'doomed' and must perish), but to the rescue of their looks and their modes . . . phoenix-like, they may rise from the 'stain on a painter's palette' and live again upon canvas, and stand forth for centuries yet to to come, the living monuments of a noble race" ("Letter from George Catlin, from the Mouth of the Yellowstone River, 1832" in J. W. McCoubrey, *American Art, 1700–1960: Sources and Documents,* Englewood Cliffs, N. J., 1965, 95).

Because of the Indians' uncertain and often hostile reactions to being painted, Catlin had to content himself with rapid sketches. Usually he painted merely the facial features and dashed in an outline of the figure, making quick pencil details of the costume. *Wan-ee-ton,* painted in 1868 after an earlier field sketch, records with care and accuracy the appearance and character of the Sioux chieftain. Today Catlin's work is important both as scientific documentation and as early American portraiture.

NHS

Alfred Jacob Miller 1810–1874

49 *Crow Indian on the Lookout,* ca. 1844

Oil on canvas, 10 x 12 inches

Provenance: David Ives Bushnell, Jr.; Peabody Museum, Harvard University, Bushnell Collection (41-72-10/442).

A pupil of Thomas Sully, Miller also studied in Paris at the Ecole des Beaux Arts. He developed a thorough knowledge of the great European masters before returning to the United States, where he established himself first in Baltimore, then New Orleans. In 1837 he accompanied the Stuart expedition into the far West and produced many watercolor sketches which he turned into finished oils in his studio after his return. *Crow Indian on the Lookout* was probably one such picture. It represents a romanticized image of the Indian as a noble savage and in so doing manifests an attitude similar to that appearing in French painting of the same period. French artists, notably Delacroix, viewed Moroccan Arabs as children of nature, living descendants of a classical heritage. Many western artists felt this way about the Indian and often referred to him in terms which were common to Rousseau and the Age of Reason.

EAP

Seth Eastman 1808–1875

50 *Live Oaks with Two Small Figures,* ca. 1850

Oil on canvas, 9⅛ x 12¼ inches

Signed lower right: S. Eastman

Provenance: David Ives Bushnell, Jr.; Peabody Museum, Harvard University, Bushnell Collection (41-72-10/75).

51 *Winnebago Wigwams,* 1850

Watercolor, 10 x 8 inches

Signed and dated lower right: S Eastman 1850

Provenance: David Ives Bushnell, Jr.; Peabody Museum, Harvard University, Bushnell Collection (41-72-10/118).

An Army officer who learned to sketch as part of his officer training, Eastman developed his talent as a topographical draughtsman and painter. He was a native of Brunswick, Maine, and attended West Point, where from 1833 to 1840 he taught drawing before serving a tour of duty at several western forts. From 1850 to 1855 he worked on illustrations for Henry R. Schoolcraft's *History and Statistical Information Respecting the . . . Indian Tribes of the United States.*

The Bushnell Collection in the Peabody Museum contains many sketches and watercolors by Eastman, who throughout his military career produced studies that documented areas of topographical interest and the disappearing way of life of the Indian. He completed several studies similar to this oil, which was probably painted in 1850 when Eastman was stationed at Camp Houston, Texas. The tree appears in many other works of this period, all in the Bushnell Collection, and is evident in *Winnebago Wigwams.*

Eastman's interest in the western landscape and its Indian inhabitants seems to have been of a reportorial and documentary nature. Unlike Carl Wimar, it was not sympathy that inspired him to record the vanishing Indian life; Eastman was, like George Catlin, more of a reporter-realist whose work at best exhibits a delicate beauty and is rarely sentimental.

EAP

Carl Wimar 1828–1862

52   *Mounted Indians Running Buffalo,* ca. 1859

Wash on paper, 9½ x 15 inches

Initialed lower right: CW

Provenance: David Ives Bushnell, Jr.; Peabody Museum, Harvard University, Bushnell Collection (41-72-10/516).

German by birth, Carl Wimar settled in St. Louis when he was fifteen. In 1846 he became a pupil of Leon Pomardee and made a trip up the Mississippi River with him in 1849. Wimar returned to Germany in 1852 and studied with Emmanuel Leutze in Düsseldorf; in 1856 he came back to St. Louis and began to paint the Plains Indians. He went on several river excursions into Indian country, and on these he would make rapid sketches, or if possible photographs; both were then employed as studies for finished oils. Wimar must have been one of the pioneers of photography in the West, but his working methods, finishing pictures in the studio, were consistent with European academic practices.

Wimar maintained an attitude toward the Indian which was, for that period in American history, basically sympathetic. Like many of his contemporaries, he looked upon them as children of nature whose way of life was being overwhelmed by the white man's westward expansion. His attempts to record Indian life were prompted by a conscious effort to keep alive the memory of that age of settlement and narrowing frontiers.

Wimar's oils secure themselves to a mid-century romantic tradition which can be cloying. But many of his preliminary sketches, such as this of *Indians Running Buffalo,* one of the artist's favorite themes, exhibit a freshness and spontaneity consistent with the drama and excitement of the subject.

EAP

George Loring Brown 1814–1889

53 *View of Naples,* 1855

Pencil, highlighted with extensive scratchwork
paper, 7⅛ x 9⅞ inches

Signed lower right: G.L.B.; dated lower left:
1855

Provenance: Giovanni Castano, Boston; Fogg
Art Museum, Harvard University, Purchase of
the William C. Heilman Fund (1956.41).

At the age of twelve George Loring Brown was
apprenticed to the Boston wood engraver,
Alonzo Hartwell; later he studied painting in
the Cambridge studio of Washington Allston.
Brown's training as a graphic artist taught
him to use the expressive potential of a linear
and tonal style, and his experience as a
painter developed his sensitivity to the subtle
nuances of light. *View of Naples,* 1855, which
dates from the last years of the artist's second
trip abroad (1839–1859), is a brilliant synthesis
of these graphic and painterly abilities.
Brown's remarkable drawing technique
caused Nathaniel Hawthorne to comment in
his *French and Italian Notebooks* (Boston,
1873): "April 22, 1858: Mr. Brown showed us
some drawings from nature, done with in-
credible care and minuteness of detail as
studies for his paintings. We complimented
him on his patience, but he said, 'Oh, it's not
patience, —it's love.' "

NHS

Benjamin Champney 1817–1907

54 *Mountain Landscape,* 1850

Pencil, highlighted with extensive scratchwork in white, on pale green paper with embossed circle printed in tones of blue shading to yellow, 10⅝ x 13¾ inches; design area 6⅜ inches.

Signed and dated lower left in circle: B. Champney, 1850

Signed lower right: B. Champney

Inscribed below circle: Scene on the Connecticut/drawn by Benj. Champney/Landscape painter/of Boston

Provenance: John Witt Randall; Fogg Art Museum, Harvard University, Bequest of John Witt Randall (1898.443).

After extended European travels, Benjamin Champney settled in Boston; later he moved permanently to North Conway, New Hampshire. In the 1850's he was recognized as the leader of a group of Boston landscape artists who met annually in North Conway with a New York group headed by John Frederick Kensett. During the last years of his life, Champney wrote *Sixty Years: Memories of Art and Artists,* a book in which he recorded valuable information about his friends and in which he described his attachment to the landscape of the North Conway region: "I write with pleasure and pride of the scenery of North Conway and Intervale. I have known it so long, and so intimately that every corner and every stretch of view is dear to me, and I am proud to consider myself almost a native, and part owner of the whole" (B. Champney, *Sixty Years: Memories of Art and Artists,* Woburn, Mass., 1900, 156-157).

NHS

Fitz Hugh Lane 1804–1865

55 *Gloucester Harbor,* ca. 1859

Oil on canvas, 24 x 38 1/16 inches

Provenance: W. Y. Balsh Gallery, Boston, 1859; Charles D. Childs, Boston, 1935; Charles E. Cotting, Boston, ca. 1935; Harvard Graduate School of Business Administration, Gift of Charles E. Cotting, 1968.

Bibliography: J. Wilmerding, *Fitz Hugh Lane,* New York, 1971, 75.

Fitz Hugh Lane was born in Gloucester in 1804. During the thirties he was an apprentice in the Boston lithography shop of William S. Pendleton. His first paintings, executed about 1840, show the influence of Robert Salmon, an English marine artist who worked in Boston from 1828 to 1842, and seventeenth-century Dutch land- and seascapes, which Lane could have seen at the Boston Athenaeum. About 1848 he returned to Gloucester, where he worked, except for summer visits to the Maine coast, until his death in 1865. Virtually forgotten for almost a century, Lane now has a place among the most important midnineteenth-century American painters.

In the best works of his maturity Lane uses luminous and hyperrealistic views of nature to express mood, and the source for this kind of ideated marine and landscape painting may lie in New England transcendental aesthetics. Emerson gives spiritual attributes to light and insists that "Every appearance in nature corresponds to some state of mind, and that state of mind can only be described by presenting the natural appearance as its picture." This may explain the compelling mood of contemplation in *Gloucester Harbor,* a painting in which the brilliant sunset seems to assume an iconic significance.

JRL

Hiram Powers 1805–1873

56 *John Farrar,* 1837

White marble, height 23 inches

Inscribed lower center rear: Prof. John Farrar by H. Powers

Provenance: Harvard University Portrait Collection, Gift of Mrs. John Farrar, 1870 (S 28).

Bibliography: C. E. Lester, *The Artist, the Merchant and the Statesman,* New York, 1845, 76-77.

57 *Luly's Hand,* 1839

White marble, 5½ inches in diameter

Provenance: Fogg Art Museum, Harvard University, Gift of Prof. J. H. Ropes (1928.115).

Bibliography: N. Hawthorne, *French and Italian Notebooks,* Boston, 1873, 308.

58 *America,* 1863

White marble, height 24¾ inches

Inscribed on back: H. Powers Sculp.

Provenance: Harvard College Collection; transferred to the Fogg Art Museum, Harvard University (1958.180).

Bibliography: N. Hawthorne, *French and Italian Notebooks,* Boston, 1873, 431; J. J. Jarves, *The Art-Idea,* New York, 1864, revised edition edited by Benjamin Rowland, Jr., Cambridge, Mass., 1960, 215; H. T. Tuckerman, *Book of Artists, American Artist Life,* New York, 1867, 290; O. Larkin, *Art and Life in America,* New York, 1946, 180; W. Craven, *Sculpture in America,* New York, 1968, 132.

59 *Robert C. Winthrop,* 1868

White marble, height 24½ inches

Inscribed on front: Robert C. Winthrop (1809–1868)

Inscribed on left shoulder: H. Powers/sculp 1868

Provenance: Harvard University Portrait Collection, Gift of Robert C. Winthrop (S 36).

60 *Henry Wadsworth Longfellow,* ca. 1868

White marble, height 24½ inches

Inscribed on left shoulder: H. Powers

Provenance: Harvard University Portrait Collection, Gift of Alice M. Longfellow and Mrs. Annie L. Thorp in fulfillment of a desire of the late Mrs. May L. Greenleaf, sister of H. W. Longfellow (S 33).

Hiram Powers, perhaps the best known of all midcentury American neoclassical sculptors, moved to Florence, Italy, in 1837. His first commission was the bust of Professor John Farrar, the Hollis Professor of Mathematics and Natural Philosophy from 1807 to 1836 at Harvard University. The artist described the difficulties he encountered working with Italian stone-cutters for the first time. "I had modelled a great number of busts in America, but with the exception of a very few, they had not been commissioned . . . I had been here [Florence] several months . . . Professor Farrar, of Cambridge, Massachusetts was resided in Florence, and he engaged his bust." Dismayed at the incompetence of his workmen, Powers related, "I sent away my men, and took up the mallet and chisel, and went to work upon Professor Farrar's bust. My blocker-out had absolutely spoiled everything; cutting away an eighth of an inch too much from nose and chin" (Lester, *The Artist*, 76-77). Soon Powers trained the workmen to copy his models faithfully. His pleasure with *Luly's Hand* (a work based on a cast of the hand of his daughter, Louisa Greenough Powers, taken five months after her birth on 10 September 1838) was recorded by Nathaniel Hawthorne in his *French and Italian Notebooks*. "June 13th, 1858: One piece of sculpture Powers exhibited, however, which was very exquisite, and such as I never saw before. Opening a desk, he took out something carefully enclosed between two layers of cotton wool, on removing which there appeared a little baby's hand most delicately represented in the whitest marble; all the dimples where the knuckles were to be, all the creases in the plump flesh, every infantile wrinkle of the soft skin, being lovingly recorded. 'The critics condemn minute representation,' said Powers; 'But you may look at this through a microscope and see if it injures the general effect.' It was the hand of his daughter, 'Luly's Hand' Powers called it, — the same that gave my own such a frank and friendly grasp when I first met 'Luly.' The sculptor made it only for himself and his wife; but so many people, he said, had insisted on having a copy, that there are now forty scattered about the world" (Hawthorne, *Notebooks*, 308).

Although Powers continued to live in Italy for the rest of his life, his patriotism remained so extreme that he regularly imported American clay for his work. Hawthorne reported seeing a bust of the allegorical female figure *America,* "September 29, 1858: . . . Powers showed me, in his studio, the model of the statue of America, which he wished the government to buy. It has great merit, and embodies the ideal of youth, freedom, progress and whatever we consider as distinctive of our country's character and destiny" (Hawthorne, *Notebooks,* 431).

American travelers in Italy flocked to Powers' studio to commission their portraits. Although no records exist to indicate that Henry Wadsworth Longfellow, who held the Smith Chair of Modern Languages at Harvard from 1836 to 1854, sat for his portrait, it is likely that the bust was modeled during the poet's last visit to Italy in 1868.

Robert C. Winthrop, a Harvard graduate who later served as Overseer for the College, ordered three marble busts of himself from the model Powers had made in 1837. In a letter to the artist, Winthrop explained that he wanted to give the busts to his wife, his stepson Mr. Weltes, and to an institution. He specified that one of the busts be clothed, as "The delicate female eye of my wife shrinks from looking upon the undraped bust of her husband" (letter dated 15 Aug. 1952 from the authorized biographer of Hiram Powers, Clara Louis Dentler, to the Registrar, Fogg Art Museum).

NHS

61 *Henry Wadsworth Longfellow,* 1871

White marble, height 29 inches

Inscribed on the back: H. W. Longfellow, 1871, Rome

Provenance: Harvard University Portrait Collection (S 52).

Bibliography: P. Hanaford, *Daughters of America,* Augusta, Maine, 1883, 298; W. G. Brown, *A List of Portraits in the Various Buildings of Harvard University,* Cambridge, Mass., 1898, 27.

Edmonia Lewis, the daughter of an American Negro and a Chippewa Indian, was a well-known sculptress in the third quarter of the nineteenth century. In her sculpture, she portrayed the public figures who defended the minority rights of the Negro and the Indian. It is fitting that she modeled the bust of the creator of the famous literary figures Hiawatha and Minnehaha, Henry Wadsworth Longfellow (1807–1882). Official records are silent as to if and when Longfellow actually sat for this portrait, although it would have been possible during his last trip abroad from 1868 to 1869. A contemporary report of 1883 suggests how the completed work was acquired by the University: "She brought with her to this country from Rome a bust of 'our poet,' said to be one of the best ever taken. It has been proposed by some of Longfellow's friends to have it put into marble for Harvard" (Hanaford, *Daughters,* 298).

NHS

Chester Harding   1792–1866

62   *Portrait of Francis Parkman,* ca. 1830

Oil on canvas, 36 x 28½ inches

Provenance: Eliza W. S. Parkman; Harvard University Portrait Collection, Bequest of Eliza W. S. Parkman, 1906 (H 132).

Bibliography: L. Huntsinger, *Harvard Portraits* (A. Burroughs, ed.), Cambridge, Mass., 1936, 106.

In 1823 a Boston lady wrote a poem celebrating the talents of Chester Harding:

Most wondrous gift, from natur's self-derived,
His genius of all foreign and deprived,
Sprung up and bloomed amid our wilds
  obscure,
And won its self-taught way to glory sure.

Harding, a personable, self-taught painter, once counseled by his grandfather that portrait painting was "little better than swindling to charge forty dollars," enjoyed immense popularity in Boston during the 1820's. Today, however, his works, like those of G. P. A. Healy, do not command the attention they deserve. Both Harding and Healy were the last major American artists to practice portraiture to the exclusion of other modes of painting. Their conclusions were not original and their work, restricted in content, was derivative. But many of their canvases, for instance this Harding *Portrait of Francis Parkman* (1788-1852), are vigorously and energetically painted and appeal through the force of the personality represented. Francis Parkman founded the Parkman Professorship at Harvard and was succeeded by his son, who became the eminent historian of the American West.

EAP

63   *Edward Tyrrel Channing,* ca. 1852

Oil on canvas, 30⁵⁄₁₆ x 25⁵⁄₁₆ inches

Provenance: Harvard University Portrait Collection; Presented to Harvard College in 1852 by a "large number of Alumni of Harvard College graduated since 1819" (H 92).

Bibliography: L. Huntsinger, *Harvard Portraits* (A. Burroughs, ed.), Cambridge, Mass., 1936, 35.

George Peter Alexander Healy was one of America's most successful portrait painters, and it is unfortunate that his work is so little known today. He was born in Boston and in 1834 went to France and studied in the atelier of Baron Gros. His talent matured quickly, and when he returned to America, Healy had achieved a continental reputation of considerable proportion, one enhanced by the fact that he had received the official patronage of Louis Philippe of France.

This portrait of Edward Tyrrel Channing (1790–1856) was probably painted in 1852; Healy was in Boston for a brief period then, and during this time such notables as Hawthorne and Longfellow sat to him (M. DeMare, *G. P. A. Healy, American Artist,* New York, 1954, 173). The portrait shows evidence of rapid execution, particularly the hastily brushed-in background, and it is possible that he finished the work before moving on to Providence. Professor Channing was the son of William and Lucy Ellery Channing of Newport, parents-in-law of Washington Allston, and occupied the Boylston Professorship of Rhetoric and Oratory at Harvard from 1819 to 1851. The date of this fine portrait seems secure; its provenance suggests that it was most likely commissioned after Professor Channing's retirement.

EAP

William Stanley Haseltine   1835–1900

64   *Dying Seagull* and *Tortoise Resting on a Log,*
1852–1854

Oil on two panels of a wood door; upper 29 x
12¾ inches; lower 25 1/16 x 12¾ inches

Signed lower right of upper panel: W. S.
Haseltine

Provenance: Door formerly of 25 Stoughton
Hall, Harvard University; Fogg Art Museum,
Harvard University (1963.163).

Bibliography: H. H. Plowden, *William Stanley
Haseltine,* London, 1947, 29.

In 1852 William Stanley Haseltine transferred
from the University of Pennsylvania to Harvard as a sophomore. His classmate, Horace
Howard Furness, remembered that Haseltine,
as an undergraduate, "was a born artist and
showed his love of painting by decorating the
walls and panels of his college rooms at
Stoughton. These pictures were preserved for
many years after he left college and were only
obliterated when time had faded out the colors" (Plowden, *Haseltine,* 29).

Two panels, *Dying Seagull* and *Tortoise Resting on a Log,* were discovered and restored in
1935 by Edward Waldo Forbes, then Director
of the Fogg Art Museum. The panels show
young Haseltine's fine and careful draughtsmanship, a quality which continued throughout much of his later work.

NHS

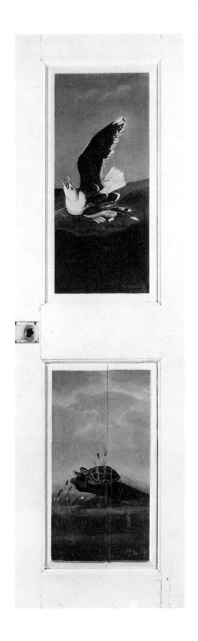

65 *Portrait of Mrs. Percival Lowell Everett,* ca. 1850

White marble, height 26½ inches

Provenance: Fogg Art Museum, Harvard University, Gift of Miss Louisa O. Everett, Miss Elizabeth Lowell Everett, and Mr. Otis Everett (1939.82).

Henry Dexter's mother forbade him to pursue a career as an artist, warning, "no one could do it who was not born under a particular star" (J. Albee, *Henry Dexter, Sculptor: A Memorial,* Cambridge, Mass., 1898, 39). Thus advised, he determined to learn a trade and became apprenticed to a blacksmith. One day a decade later his friend, the portrait painter Francis Alexander, pointed out a gentleman saying, "That is Greenough, the sculptor. By the way, he is going to Italy, and you had better get his clay, it may be useful to you sometime" (H. T. Tuckerman, *Book of Artists, American Artist Life,* New York, 1867, 587). A letter from a friend of Dexter's to Tuckerman describes the outcome of Alexander's suggestion: "Mr. Dexter's busts soon commanded five hundred dollars. He is justified in grateful acknowledgement of the liberality of the distinguished gentlemen of Boston who have put his talent in requisition. Other states and cities besides his own have amply shown their appreciation of his genius. A long array of noble names might be pointed to with pride" (Tuckerman, *Book of Artists,* 588).

NHS

Eastman Johnson 1824–1906

66 *Hon. Robert C. Winthrop,* 1845

Crayon on buff paper, 10¾ x 8 inches

Signed and dated (covered by frame): J. E. Johnson, del. January 22, 1845

Provenance: Fogg Art Museum, Harvard University, Bequest of Meta and Paul J. Sachs (1965.124).

67 *Mrs. James (Dolly) Madison,* 1846

Crayon heightened with white on buff paper, 21¼ x 14¾ inches

Signed and dated lower right: E. Johnson/Mch. 1846

Provenance: Grenville L. Winthrop; Fogg Art Museum, Harvard University, Bequest of Grenville L. Winthrop (1943.572).

Eastman Johnson was born in Lowell, Maine, and spent his early years in northern New England. In 1840 or 1841 he decided to become a painter and was placed by his father in a lithography shop in Boston, possibly Bufford's, where Winslow Homer also served an early apprenticeship. He soon tired of the city and this training, however, and returned home where he began to do small crayon portraits. Sometime in 1844 or 1845 Johnson moved to Washington, D. C., and in a short time he became established as a portraitist. Some of his sitters represented the city's political and social elite, and Johnson occasionally did their portraits not as commissions but, according to John I. H. Baur, purely for his own collection (J. I. H. Baur, *Eastman Johnson* [exhibition catalogue], Brooklyn Museum, New York, 1946). The portrait of Mrs. Madison is an example of this kind, while that of Mr. Winthrop was probably commissioned.

These portraits served the artist as valuable advertisements, and not only attracted other sitters but apparently became popular in their own right. Daniel Webster commissioned a replica of the portrait of Mrs. Madison when Johnson refused to sell him his original study.

The marked preference for a black and white medium probably had much to do with Johnson's early lithographic training. In these fine early portraits he has exploited the heavy texture of the paper with the crayon to great advantage, creating an image soft in chiaroscuro effects and modeling but fully three-dimensional in aspect. Mrs. Madison, the finer of the two, is evenly lighted, and the overall appearance of the portrait, as Baur notes, is closer to mezzotint than drawing (Baur, *Eastman Johnson,* 7).

EAP

Randolph Rogers   1825–1892

68   *Nydia,* 1859

White marble, height 35½ inches

Signed and dated on basket: Randolph Rogers /Rome 1859

Provenance: Fogg Art Museum, Harvard University, Gift of Mr. Harry Sachs (1922.136).

Bibliography: E. Bulwer-Lytton, *The Last Days of Pompeii,* London, 1834, reprint New York, 1946, 348; M. F. Thorp, *The Literary Sculptors,* Durham, N. C., 1965, 175, illus. frontispiece; W. Craven, *Sculpture in America,* 1968, 314; J. Howat, J. Wilmerding, N. Spassky, and others, *19th-Century America: Paintings and Sculpture* [exhibition catalogue], The Metropolitan Museum of Art, New York, 1970, 114; R. Lynes, *The Art Makers of the Nineteenth Century,* New York, 1970, 147, reprod. 148.

Nydia, the blind flower girl of Pompeii, was based on the female protagonist of Edward Bulwer-Lytton's *The Last Days of Pompeii,* a popular novel of the nineteenth century. In his book the author describes the plight of the sightless Nydia on the day in A. D. 79 when Vesuvius erupted and destroyed the city of Pompeii. "Poor Girl—her courage was beautiful to behold—and Fate seemed to favour one so helpless! The boiling torrents touched her not, save by the general rain which accompanied them; the huge fragments of scoria shivered the pavement before and beside her, but spared that frail form; and when the lesser ashes fell over her, she shook them away with a slight tremor, and dauntlessly resumed her course. Weak, exposed, yet fearless, supported but by one wish, she was a very emblem of Psyche in her wanderings; of Hope, walking through the Valley of the Shadow; of the Soul itself—lone, but undaunted, amidst the dangers and the snares of life!" (Bulwer-Lytton, *Pompeii,* 348).

The statue of the blind *Nydia* captured the imagination of the nineteenth-century American public. The sale of approximately one hundred replicas of the original work reflected the prevailing taste for sentimental and moral themes in art.

NHS

Winslow Homer 1836–1910

69 *Pitching Horseshoes,* 1865

Oil on canvas, 26¾ x 53¹¹⁄₁₆ inches

Signed and dated lower right: Winslow Homer 1865

Provenance: Abijah Curtiss; Frederic H. Curtiss; Fogg Art Museum, Harvard University, Gift of Mr. and Mrs. Frederic H. Curtiss (1940.298).

Bibliography: W. A. Downes, *Winslow Homer,* Boston, 1911, 52-53; L. Goodrich, *Winslow Homer,* New York, 1944, 21.

Homer began painting in oils in 1862. This canvas, one of his ambitious early works, depicts a group of volunteers from New York wearing the uniform of the Hawkins Zouaves at a camp near Washington, perhaps in Alexandria. The painting is an illustration of everyday camp life, and only the uniforms evoke a sense of military romanticism.

In spite of Goodrich's comments that "with its photographic realism, uncompromising clarity, and hard bright local colors" it is "innocent of artistic quality" (Goodrich, *Homer,* 21), *Pitching Horseshoes* displays elements which Homer would develop later. Homer's representation of a specific activity is not mere anecdote; *Pitching Horseshoes* attempts to reveal his understanding about one side of the human experience. The feeling of bright sunlight is also something that he would refine and improve in the later Adirondacks watercolors (see Nos. 100-107).

KCB

John Rogers   1829–1904

70   *Council of War,* 1868

Plaster painted grey, height 24 inches

Inscribed on base: Council of War
Inscribed on back: Patented/March 31, 1868
Inscribed on left front: John Rogers/New York

Provenance: Widener Library; Houghton Library, Harvard University.

Bibliography: C. Smith, *Rogers Groups,* Boston 1934, 73; D. Wallace, *John Rogers, The People's Sculptor,* Middletown, Conn., 1967, 218–220; W. Craven, *Sculpture in America,* New York, 1968, 363; R. Lynes, *The Art Makers of the Nineteenth Century,* New York, 1970, 149.

During his brief one-year stay in Europe Rogers wrote to his father from Rome, "I don't think I shall ever get into the classic style. I do not take to it. I think my best course is to pursue the path that I have begun and make small figures in bronze or very nice plaster . . . and not attempt any 'high art,' for I shall certainly step out of my depth if I do" (Lynes, *Art Makers,* 147). This decision proved to be wise; the popularity of the moderately priced (fourteen dollars) mass-produced "Rogers Groups" resulted in the sale of approximately 100,000 statuettes. Based on human interest themes which ranged from the serious *(The Slave Auction)* to the humorous *(The Checker Players)* his works were the three-dimensional counterpart of the genre paintings of Bingham and Mount.

Council of War was one of Rogers' first attempts to portray well-known public figures. It depicts General Grant, Abraham Lincoln, and Secretary of War Stanton. Rogers' effort was so successful that Stanton wrote him in praise of the work: "You were especially fortunate in your execution of the figure of President Lincoln. In form and feature it surpasses any effort to embody the expression of the great man which I have seen" (Smith, *Rogers,* 73).

NHS

James McDougall Hart 1828–1901

71 *Sunday P. M.,* 1857

Oil on canvas, 10¾ x 18¼ inches

Signed and dated lower left: Jas M. Hart 57

Provenance: Fogg Art Museum, Harvard University, Bequest of Mrs. William Hayes Fogg (1895.705).

Sunday P. M., 1857, painted four years after Hart's return from study in Europe, typifies the artist's interest in anecdotal pastoral scenes. To enliven his straightforward, naturalistic landscapes the artist often added human and animal figures, a practice which occasioned his older brother William, who was also a landscape painter, to remark in the brogue of his native Scotland, "Jeames, he's a fair mon but he connot paint a coo" (Museum of Fine Arts, Boston, *M. and M. Karolik Collection of American Paintings 1815–1865,* Cambridge, Mass., 1949, 292). Nevertheless, Hart's careful country landscapes were eagerly collected and prized by the people of New York who were dismayed by the rapid spread of industry into the vanishing wilderness along the Hudson River.

NHS

Attributed to
Sanford Robinson Gifford   1823–1880

72   *Storm King on the Hudson,* ca. 1866

Oil on canvas, 10¼ x 18½ inches

Provenance: Mrs. William Hayes Fogg; Fogg
Art Museum, Harvard University, Bequest of
Mrs. William Hayes Fogg (1895.703).

Sanford Robinson Gifford belongs to the "second generation" of Hudson River School painters. He was raised on the banks of the Hudson,
attended Brown University in 1842-44, and in
1845 studied drawings with John Rubens Smith
in New York City. In 1855-56 during the first
of two trips to Europe, he joined Bierstadt and
Whittredge in Italy. Between the Civil War,
in which he was one of the few artists to par-
ticipate actively, and his return to Europe in
1868, Gifford painted scenes of the Catskills
and the Hudson.

Unsigned and undated, *Storm King on the
Hudson* is probably the work listed without
dimensions or attribution in the Fogg Bequest
as *Autumn Near West Point.* The back-lit
autumn trees in the lower left of this painting
recall the work of J. F. Kensett (see No. 73)
whose *View of Storm King From Fort Putnam,*
1857 (Metropolitan Museum of Art) serves to
identify the location of the view in the Fogg's
picture. The beached boat with figures is com-
parable to the fishing boats in another view
of *Storm King on the Hudson,* 1866 (National
Collection of the Fine Arts) by Samuel Coleman, whose work is also represented in the
Fogg Bequest. For reasons of style, composition, and color, however, this painting is here
attributed to Gifford.

Cikovsky states that "the perimeters [of his
art] were close and clearly marked . . . in order
that Gifford could devote himself to subtleties
of color and pictorial design that . . . lay at
the center of his artistic temperament" (N.
Cikovsky, Jr., *Sanford Robinson Gifford 1823–
1880* [exhibition catalogue], Hirschl and
Adler, New York, 1970, 18). Basic to the Fogg
painting are pictorial elements commonly
used by Gifford: the rowboat with figures in
In the Green Mountains (Cikovsky, *Gifford,*
fig. 19), the convention for describing the
river's edge as a series of concave forms in
Landscape with Stottsville in the Background
(Albany Institute of History and Art), and the
long reflections of the sailboats in *Sunset on
the Hudson* (Wadsworth Atheneum, Hartford).

More basic to Gifford's work — regardless of
subject — is the mood he establishes with color
and luminosity. Cikovsky describes this element as "the binding medium for these
[pictorial] elements, bathing everything in
tinctured light, and as a result achieving that
condition of unity that he admired in Turner
and Barbizon landscapes" (Cikovsky, *Gifford,*
16). James Jackson Jarves was more critical
when he noted in 1864 that "Gifford has an
opulant sense of color, but its tone is artificial
and strained, often of a lively or brimstone
tint" (J. J. Jarves, *The Art Idea,* ed. B. Rowland,
Jr., Cambridge, Mass., 1960, 193). Although
Leander's Tower on the Bosphorus (see No. 80)
is a more extreme example of this sunset
coloring, the obvious concern for the effects
of sunset on the atmosphere supports this
attribution to Gifford.

KCB

John Frederick Kensett 1816–1872

73 *Mountain and Lake,* ca. 1860

Oil on canvas, 13¾ x 23¾ inches

Signed lower left: Kensett J. F.

Provenance: Mrs. William Hayes Fogg; Fogg Art Museum, Harvard University, Bequest of Mrs. William Hayes Fogg (1895.708).

John Frederick Kensett is considered a leader of the "second generation" Hudson River School during the mid-nineteenth century. The widespread popularity of his quiet and subtle landscapes of the eastern countryside is impressive in an age which was accustomed to the dramatic panoramas of Frederick Church and Albert Bierstadt. Kensett's close friend George W. Curtis, editor of "The Easy Chair" in *Harper's Magazine,* explained Kensett's curious appeal: "All his pictures are biographical, for they reveal the fidelity, the tenderness, and the sweet serenity of his nature" (J. T. Flexner, *That Wilder Image,* New York, 1962, 146).

Mountain and Lake is signed but not dated. The simple planar composition and the economy of picturesque detail within this landscape associate it with Kensett's late works of the 1860's, which are filled with a sense of solitude and space.

NHS

74 *Rocky Mountains, "Lander's" (Frémont?) Peak*, 1863

Oil on canvas, 43½ x 35½ inches

Signed and dated lower left: ABierstadt [AB in monogram]

Provenance: Fogg Art Museum, Harvard University, Bequest of Mrs. William Hayes Fogg (1895.698).

Bibliography: R. S. Trump, *Life and Works of Albert Bierstadt,* unpublished dissertation, The Ohio State University, 1963, 217; G. Hendricks, "The First Three Western Journeys of Albert Bierstadt," *The Art Bulletin,* 66, 1964, 338, fn. 28, app. 14, fig. 5.

75 *Landscape,* 1868

Oil on canvavs, 12⅝ x 15⅞₆ inches

Signed and dated lower right: AB 68

Provenance: Fogg Art Museum, Harvard University, Gift of Mr. and Mrs. Frederick H. Curtiss (1940.299).

Bibliography: R. S. Trump, *Life and Works of Albert Bierstadt,* unpublished dissertation, The Ohio State University, 1963, 221; G. Davidson, P. Hattis, T. Stebbins, *Luminious Landscape: The American Study of Light 1860–1875* [exhibition catalogue], Fogg Art Museum, Cambridge, Mass., 1966, 16.

76 *John Tyndall,* ca. 1865

Watercolor with overglaze of oil and varnish on white paper, 5¼ x 3⅛ inches

Inscribed upper right: John Tyndall/AETAT 45 BY AB

Provenance: Fogg Art Museum, Harvard University, Gift of Dr. Thomas Barbour (1939.185).

Bibliography: R. S. Trump, *The Life and Works of Albert Bierstadt,* unpublished dissertation, The Ohio State University, 1963, 218.

"I am delighted with the scenery," Bierstadt wrote to *The Crayon* in 1861 while he was on the Lander Expedition to the Rocky Mountains. "The mountains are very fine; and seen from the plains they resemble very much the Bernese Alps.... Their jagged summits, covered with snow and mingling with the clouds, present a scene which every lover of landscape would gaze upon with unqualified delight" (A. Bierstadt, letter published in *The Crayon,* New York, Jan. 1861, 287). *Rocky Mountains "Lander's" (Frémont?) Peak* translates Bierstadt's prose into paint and suggests the visual impact of the colossal mountain range. Origi-

nally called *Rocky Mountains, Lander's Peak* in honor of the expedition leader Colonel F. W. Lander, the title of the work has been amended to correspond to the actual name of the mountain identified as Frémont's Peak. Bierstadt's paintings of the western scenery established his reputation as "the most talked about artist in New York" (Mrs. T. B. Aldrich, *Crowding Memories,* Cambridge, Mass., 1920, 22).

By 1868 Bierstadt had made two sketching tours to the West. His landscapes were often misunderstood to be faithful topographical transcriptions of an actual landscape; however, they were often produced by a composite technique. *Landscape* was painted either from memory or with the aid of sketches and photographs while the artist was living in Rome in 1868. Originally titled *Lake Tahoe,* it combines views found in his other landscapes of Yosemite Valley and of the Swiss Matterhorn. Fitz Hugh Ludlow, Bierstadt's traveling companion, described his similar need, as a writer, to reorganize the landscape. "I have been betrayed into the artistic error . . . of painting more into my picture than I could see from my campstool; of adding after experience to the present facts of vision . . . to see the Rocky Mountains means so much more than the view of any one mighty ridge or peak" (F. H. Ludlow, *Heart of the Continent,* Cambrige, Mass., 1870, 146). It was this lyric quality of the writers and painters of the West which captured the imagination of the nineteenth-century American public. It is uncertain if and when John Tyndall, the great physicist of the Royal Academy, sat for this portrait by Bierstadt. However, it is likely that the two men knew each other, for they shared an avid interest in mountain climbing. Both men were fascinated with the atmospheric effects and cloud formations they observed in the mountain ranges of the Swiss Alps. Tyndall's publications, which included *Notes on Light* and *The Forms of Water in Clouds and Rivers,* scientifically documented those atmospheric effects which were used as a vehicle for dramatic expression in the works of Bierstadt and his friend Longfellow. The latter recorded in his diary entry for 1 September 1871, "Read in Tyndall's Swiss Sketches — climbing the Matterhorn and other perilous peaks. His descriptions of sky-effects are very beautiful" (S. Longfellow, *Life of Henry Wadsworth Longfellow,* Boston, 1886, III, 185).

NHS

77 *Philip Preparing the Funeral of Pompey the Great,* 1867

Ink and pencil on paper; the drawing is enclosed in an oval set within a gilt decorated border; oval, 10 x 12⅞₁₆ inches

Overall paper dimensions: 12⅞ x 17¾ inches

Signed lower right: W. Rimmer 1867

Inscribed lower left: Philip preparing the funeral of Pompey the Great — see Plutarch

Provenance: Fogg Art Museum, Harvard University, Gift of Mrs. Henry Simonds (1921.27).

Bibliography: L. Kirstein (intro.), *William Rimmer* [exhibition catalogue], Whitney Museum of American Art, New York, and the Museum of Fine Arts, Boston, 1946-1947, no. 75; B. Hayes, Jr., *The American Line* [exhibition catalogue], Addison Gallery of American Art, Phillips Academy, Andover, Mass., no. 48.

78 *To the Charge,* 1874

Oil on cardboard, 12⅛ x 18¼ inches

Signed and dated lower right: W. Rimmer 1874

Inscribed lower right: Sketch

Provenance: Fogg Art Museum, Harvard University, Purchase of the Louise E. Bettens Fund (1936.10.1).

Within a lifetime of sixty-three years, William Rimmer worked variously as a cobbler, physician, anatomist, lithographer, sculptor, painter, and lecturer. Largely self-taught, Rimmer distinguished himself in all these fields. Plutarch's description of Pompey's death and burial appealed to Rimmer's eccentric taste for the fantastic. Pompey, the great Roman general, was murdered by Septimus, Salvius, and Achillas who, according to Plutarch, "cut off Pompey's head, and threw the rest of his body overboard, leaving it naked upon the shore, to be viewed by any that had the

curiosity to see so sad a spectacle. Philip stayed by and watched till they had glutted their eyes in viewing it; and then washing it with sea water, having nothing else, he wrapped it in a shirt of his own for a winding-sheet. Then seeking up and down about the sands, at last he found some rotten planks of a little fisher boat, not much, but yet enough to make up a funeral pile for a naked body and that not quite entire" (A. H. Clough, ed., *Plutarch's Lives: The Translation Called Dryden's, New York,* 1911, IV, 169). Rimmer translated Plutarch's description into visual terms by placing anatomically delineated figures, vastly separated in scale, within a landscape dramatized by extreme foreshortening.

To the Charge, painted five years before the artist's death, combines Rimmer's anatomical knowledge and his lithographer's sensitivity to light and dark with his powerful and eccentric imagination to portray superbly the dramatic action of this battle scene.

NHS

John La Farge 1835–1910

79 *Still Life with Chinese Vase of Roses,* ca. 1860

Watercolor, 16⅛ x 16 inches

Provenance: Grenville L. Winthrop; Fogg Art Museum, Harvard University, Bequest of Grenville L. Winthrop (1943.310).

La Farge traveled abroad in 1856, where he worked briefly in the studio of Couture, and returned to the United States in the winter of 1857–58. By 1859 he had returned to Newport and settled down in lodgings with William Morris Hunt and William and Henry James.

Still Life with Chinese Vase of Roses was probably painted in 1860. It displays precise drawing and achieves a radiance of light from the petals, although it retains a quality of stiffness which does not appear in later examples of water lilies. La Farge noted: "I painted flowers to get the relation between the softness and the brittleness of the flower, and the hardness of the bowl, or whatever it might be, in which the flower might be placed. Instead of arranging my subject, which is the usual studio way, I had it placed for me by chance, with any background and any light . . . . Flower painting was in great part a study; that is a means of teaching myself many of the difficulties of painting" (quoted in R. Cortissoz, *Exhibition of the Work of John La Farge,* Metropolitan Museum of Art, New York, 1936, 8).

La Farge is most appreciated for his stained glass windows, but his work also includes landscapes and large murals. It is interesting that a commission for a window in Harvard's Memorial Hall provided the impetus for his first experiments in stained glass.

KCB

Sanford Robinson Gifford   1823–1880

80   *Leander's Tower on the Bosphorus,* 1876

Oil on canvas, 18½ x 38½ inches

Signed and dated lower right: S. R. Gifford, 1876

Provenance: William Hayes Fogg; Fogg Art Museum, Harvard University, Bequest of Mrs. William Hayes Fogg (1895.716).

Bibliography: Metropolitan Museum of Art, *Memorial Catalogue of the Paintings of Sanford Robinson Gifford N.A.,* New York, 1881, no. 645; N. Cikovsky, Jr., *Sanford Robinson Gifford (1823–1880)* [exhibition catalogue], Hirschl and Adler, New York, 1970-71, no. 57, fig. 77.

During his third trip abroad (1868–1869), Gifford ventured off the well-traveled artists' route through Switzerland, France, Italy, and Greece to visit Syria, Lebanon, Egypt, and Turkey. The setting of *Leander's Tower on the Bosphorus* is based on his travels in the Near East; the title refers to the myth of Hero and Leander. Every night Hero, the Priestess of Aphrodite in Sestus, lit a torch on top of a tower to guide Leander as he swam to her across the Hellespont. During a storm the light was blown out by the wind. Leander perished, and Hero, upon finding his body washed up on the shore, killed herself. Gifford, a skilled draughtsman, renders the scenic detail with meticulous care. Characteristic of the artist's later work of the 1870's, the canvas is dominated by wide expanses of sea and sky. These areas reveal Gifford's deep concern for the effects of light and atmosphere. His close friend, the painter J. Alden Weir, reminisced, "Gifford loved the light. His finest impressions were those derived from the landscape when the air is charged with an effulgence of irruptive and glowing light .... Gifford's art was poetic and reminiscent. It was not realistic in the formal sense. It was nature passed through the alembic of a finely-organized sensibility" (Metropolitan Museum, *Memorial,* 9).

NHS

William Morris Hunt 1824–1879

81 *Jean Louis Rodolphe Agassiz,* ca. 1860–1870

Oil on canvas, 21⅞ x 18 inches

Signed lower left in monogram

Provenance: Harvard University Portrait Collection, Gift of Mrs. Louis Agassiz Shaw (H 486).

82 *Niagara Falls,* ca. 1878

Pastel on paper, 9¹³⁄₁₆ x 15¼ inches

Provenance: Dorothea Simmons; Fogg Art Museum, Harvard University, Gift of the Trustees of the Naushon Trust (residual legatees under the will of Dorothea Simmons) (1963.33).

83 *Niagara Falls,* ca. 1878

Pastel on paper, 11¼ x 8⅞ inches

Provenance: Dorothea Simmons; Fogg Art Museum, Harvard University, Gift of the Trustees of the Naushon Trust (residual legatees under the will of Dorothea Simmons) (1963.34).

In 1843, Hunt's widowed mother, concerned about her son's health during his third undistinguished year at Harvard, took William and his younger brother Richard (who later became a leading American architect) to Europe. While traveling abroad, William studied art in Rome, Düsseldorf, and Paris. In Paris he entered the studio of Thomas Couture, but soon left to join J. F. Millet in Barbizon.

Hunt believed that portraiture should be based less on "scrutinizing" than on "perception" (W. M. Hunt, *Talks on Art,* 2nd ed. compiled by H. M. Knowlton, Boston, 1883, 40). In his portrait of *Jean Louis Rodolphe Agassiz* (1807–1873), the great Swiss naturalist and the founder of the Agassiz Museum of Comparative Zoology at Harvard, Hunt preserved the spontaneity of a preliminary sketch. The artist's explanation of his technique to his students reflects the influence of his earlier study with Millet. "Have faith that the simple mass will produce the effect....If you want to make an impression you must sacrifice as many details as possible. Keep your figure strong and undisturbed by little things that hinder" (Hunt, *Talks,* 49, 58).

Feeling the need for change and rest, Hunt traveled to Niagara Falls in early June of 1878. The two pastel drawings of Niagara Falls date from this trip. They were sketched directly from nature and in the medium the artist believed to be the best for preliminary studies. They demonstrate Hunt's brilliant technical ability to capture the bursting energy and surging power of his famous subject. A pupil reported seeing him at the Falls and wrote back to Boston: "Mr. Hunt says that there is nothing like Niagara in June....He is doing a great deal of work, oil painting and pastel, which the last he likes extremely for out-of-door sketching" (H. M. Knowlton, *Art Life of William Morris Hunt,* Boston, 1899, 122).

NHS

William Trost Richards 1833–1905

84 *Rocks and Cliffs near the Sea*, ca. 1885-1890

Watercolor on cream paper, 12 x 23⅞ inches

Signed lower right: W. T. Richards

Provenance: Mrs. William T. Brewster (artist's daughter); National Academy of Design; Fogg Art Museum, Harvard University, Presented by the National Academy of Design from the Mrs. William T. Brewster Bequest (1954.27).

85 *Seascape*

Brown wash on buff paper, 6 x 10¼ inches

Provenance: Mrs. William T. Brewster; National Academy of Design; Fogg Art Museum, Harvard University, Presented by the National Academy of Design from the Mrs. William T. Brewster Bequest (1954.19.2).

86 *Seascape*

Brown wash on buff paper, 6 x 10¼ inches

Provenance: Mrs. William T. Brewster; National Academy of Design; Fogg Art Museum, Harvard University, Presented by the National Academy of Design from the Mrs. William T. Brewster Bequest (1954.19.3).

87 *Seascape*

Brown wash on buff paper, 6 x 10¼ inches

Provenance: Mrs. William T. Brewster; National Academy of Design; Fogg Art Museum, Harvard University, Presented by the National Academy of Design from the Mrs. William T. Brewster Bequest (1954.19.4).

Raised near Philadelphia, Richards made a trip to Paris, Florence, and Rome in 1853. He taught George Lambdin in 1860, visited Darmstadt and Düsseldorf in 1866, and in the mid-1870's established himself at "Gray Cliff" on Conanicutt Island off Newport. He spent two years in England—from 1878 to 1880—painting the coast, which was to be a favorite subject of his thereafter, and from 1885 to 1890 he made summer trips to the British Isles.

Richards began to devote much of his time to watercolor in the 1870's. Both the art of Turner and the poetry of Wordsworth influenced his view of nature. He was a proponent of the ideas of John Ruskin and consistently tried to give each object its precise form and intensity of local color. *Rocks and Cliffs near the Sea* is frankly realistic and marked by its composition and the drawing of detail. Although color was not usually his strong point, the cool combination of blues and greens enlivened by the rainbow makes this an outstanding work. It is difficult to date, but it is possible that it stems from his two-year trip to England in 1878.

The Fogg owns a set of three sepia-colored *Seascapes.* The island subject and virtuosity of handling suggest that the watercolors may have been painted during a summer trip to the Jersey Islands in the late 1880's.

Dramatic light and texture are conveyed with skillful control of the medium, and unlike *Rocks and Cliffs near the Sea,* there is only a touch of preliminary drawing. Both the small size and the monochrome coloring facilitate the spontaneous transcription of the water's movement and the dazzling effects of light, but it is the use of the white of the paper to achieve a sparkling quality without scraping the surface with a knife that was the special achievement of the late nineteenth-century artists.

KCB

Mary S. Cassatt 1844–1926

88 *Girl on a Settee with Black Dog,* 1875

Oil on panel, 13¾ x 10½ inches

Signed and dated upper left: M. S. Cassatt, Paris 1875

Provenance: Mr. and Mrs. Peter I. B. Lavan; Fogg Art Museum, Harvard University, Gift of Mr. and Mrs. Peter I. B. Lavan (1961.159).

The decade of the 1870's was the period of Impressionist innovation, when Paris was the center of the art world. Mary Cassatt is the major American figure to have been caught up in the movement of the Independents. Her work was first accepted at the Salon of 1872, and she moved to Paris in 1874 and was joined by her parents and her sister in 1877. She lived the balance of her life in France. At first she worked in the studio of Charles Chaplin, but in 1877 she attracted Degas' attention and began to work under him as part of the Independents.

This picture, painted when she was thirty-one, indicates the beginning of her maturity as an artist, but predates this association with Degas. The woman and the couch are similar to those seen in *Mrs. Duffee Seated on a Striped Sofa Reading,* 1876 (Museum of Fine Arts, Boston). The sitter is treated in a close-up of relaxation and in a comfortable environment. Two characteristics, later to be disciplined and developed under the influence of Degas and the decorative compositions of Japanese prints, were the free application of paint and the interest in pattern as evidenced by the striped material.

KCB

William Michael Harnett 1848–1892

89 *Still Life with Bric-a-Brac,* 1878

Oil on canvas, 31 x 41¼ inches

Signed and dated lower left: W. M. Harnett, 1878

Provenance: Commissioned by William H. Folwell, Philadelphia; Grenville L. Winthrop; Fogg Art Museum, Harvard University, Gift of Grenville L. Winthrop (1942.220).

Bibliography: A. Frankenstein, *After the Hunt: William Harnett and Other American Still Life Painters, 1870–1900,* Berkeley and Los Angeles, 1953, 183; W. Gerdts, "The Bric-a-Brac Still Life," *Antiques,* 1971, 747, fig. 745; W. Gerdts and R. Burke, *American Still Life Painting,* New York, 1971, 138, 135, fig. 10-5.

90 *Head of a Woman,* 1881

Pencil on paper, 19½ x 16¼ inches

Signed and dated lower right: $\frac{|W|}{|M|}$ Munchen '81

Provenance: Fogg Art Museum, Harvard University, Bequest of Meta and Paul J. Sachs (1965.120).

Bibliography: A. Frankenstein, *After the Hunt: William Harnett and Other American Still Life Painters, 1870–1900,* Berkeley and Los Angeles, 1953, 63.

Between the ages of seventeen and twenty-seven, Harnett supported himself as a silver engraver in Philadelphia and New York, while studying drawing in the night classes of the Pennsylvania Academy of Art (1865–1869) and in New York at both the National Academy of Design and the Cooper Union (1869–1875). In 1875 Harnett finally abandoned his profession of silver engraver for that of an artist. For the next five years he supported himself in Philadelphia as a still-life painter. *Still Life with Bric-a-Brac,* 1878, dates from the end of this first period of his career. Generally the artist used his own possessions as models for his paintings; however, in this rare instance, Harnett used objects belonging to the bric-a-brac collection of William Folwell, a wealthy Philadelphia textile merchant who commissioned the work. In 1955 six of these objects were purchased from Folwell's daughter, Mrs. H. Allen Barton of Rye, New York, who explained in a letter: "The plate has a picture of a girl on it instead of birds as in the painting, but that is because Mr. Harnett decided he didn't

want a girl's head, but he did want the blue edge, so he just put in the birds." The artist's style belongs to the Philadelphia school of still life, established fifty years earlier by James and Raphaelle Peale. Harnett's work is distinguished by its sensitivity to tonal modulation and surface textures.

By 1880 Harnett was able to finance a trip abroad and spent the next six years in Europe, living in Munich much of the time. *Head of a Woman* dates from the first year of his stay. The drawing affords a rare glimpse of Harnett as a draughtsman working with a live model. The same keenness of observation which characterizes his larger painted works is present within the intimate scale of this drawing.

NHS

H. Thomas Bromley   active 1897

91   *Still Life with Duck,* ca. 1890

Oil on panel (board on cradled panel), 22¹³⁄₁₆ x 18¼ inches

Signed lower left on painted scrap of paper with the monogram associated with the painter William Michael Harnett: |ᵂ⁄ᴹ|

Provenance: Fogg Art Museum, Harvard University, Gift of Charles K. Lock (1961.155).

Bibliography: A. Frankenstein, *After the Hunt: William Harnett and Other American Still Life Painters, 1870–1900,* Berkeley and Los Angeles, 1953, 183.

The curious presence of Harnett's monogram was responsible for an initial attribution of *Still Life with Duck* to Harnett. Although the still life contains motifs borrowed from Harnett (the mallard duck, the splintered board with scraps of attached paper, and the use of words and numbers), Harnett's particular sense of the object and his characteristic surface organization are lacking. The painting should be considered as part of the still life tradition which Harnett dominated during the last quarter of the nineteenth century and which produced a flurry of imitators.

The attribution to Bromley was made by Charles C. Cunningham, Director of the Art Institute of Chicago, in a letter of 8 April 1967 to John Coolidge, then Director of the Fogg Art Museum. Cunningham based his attribution on a comparison of *Still Life with Duck* to a similar still life he saw at Houthakker's in Amsterdam and which bore a tag signed H. Thomas Bromley and addressed Birmingham, Alabama, 1897. On the strength of this comparison Cunningham wrote, "I can't lay my hand on my heart and swear that it is the same artist, but I would be pretty sure."

NHS

James Abbott McNeil Whistler   1834–1903

92   *Nocturne in Blue and Silver, No. 1,* 1877

Oil on canvas, 17½ x 23¼ inches

Signed lower right with monogram in the form of a Japanese character

Provenance: Mrs. F. R. Leyland; Tulane University; Grenville L. Winthrop; Fogg Art Museum, Harvard University, Bequest of Grenville L. Winthrop (1943.176).

Bibliography: G. R. Dennis and T. R. Way, *The Art of James McNeil Whistler,* London, 1905, 59; E. R. Pennell and J. Pennell, *The Life of James McNeil Whistler,* London, 1908, 236.

93   *Nocturne in Grey and Gold; Chelsea Snow,* 1878

Oil on canvas, 17½ x 24 inches

Provenance: Grenville L. Winthrop; Fogg Art Museum, Harvard University, Bequest of Grenville L. Winthrop (1943.172).

Bibliography: D. Holden, *Whistler Landscapes and Seascapes,* New York, 1970, 46.

Whistler is the first well-known champion of art for art's sake. Though once he was a friend of Courbet's, he later reacted against this form of realism. Whistler's position that artists should rule themselves rather than be ruled by critics led him to instigate in 1878 a suit against the critic Ruskin. *Nocturne in Blue and Silver, No. 1* was one of the works which was exhibited at the famous trial.

This work dates from the same period as the Peacock Room (Freer Gallery). It was first exhibited at the Grosvenor Gallery in 1877, and Pennell notes that it was eventually "sent to Mrs. Leyland in lieu of a former commission, the amount of which was a hundred and fifty guineas." (Pennell, *Whistler,* 236). Mrs. Leyland's husband had been the artist's major patron and was his chief creditor at the time of his bankruptcy after Whistler was assessed the court costs of the trial.

The *Nocturne* deals with the subject of night in London and views Battersea Reach in Chelsea. Whistler's paintings of Battersea Bridge, however, better reveal his interest and debt to Hiroshige. The title is meant to make an analogy with music and underlines the essentially poetic outlook and the content of mood.

Nocturne in Grey and Gold; Chelsea Snow was painted in the year of the Ruskin trial. Although the subject is also of Chelsea and of night and atmosphere, the tones are warmer than the blues of the water scenes. In both works shapes lose their definition as light and atmosphere become the main components of the composition. Small touches of light float against the warm tones of the darkness, and their arrangement testifies to Whistler's basically formal and intellectual approach to composition. Luminous effects of light and shifting color, achieved with thinly applied paint over colored grounds, are key to the success of this painting.

Whistler commented on this painting in *The Red Rag* published in the *World*, 1878: "My picture of a *Harmony in Grey and Gold* is an illustration of my meaning — a snow scene with a single black figure and a lighted tavern. I care nothing for the past, present or future of the black figure, placed there because the black was wanted at that spot. All I know is that my combination of grey and gold is the basis of my picture" (Holden, *Whistler*, 46).

KCB

94   *Brown and Gold; Lillie in our Alley,* 1898

Oil on canvas, 20 x 12 inches

Provenance: John James Cowan; Tulane University; Grenville L. Winthrop; Fogg Art Museum, Harvard University, Bequest of Grenville L. Winthrop (1943.177).

Toward the end of his life Whistler painted sketches of children. Pennell describes how "the children of the street adored him, that is, the children of Chelsea and Fitzroy Street who were used to artists and knew him well" (Pennell, *Whistler,* 204-205). That Whistler returned their affection is evident in this example.

Sweet notes that Whistler painted four portraits of this model, Lily Pamington, from 1896 to 1900, and that they were probably made at his Fitzroy Street studio in Soho. The title might be an allusion to the song, "Sally in Our Alley" (F. A. Sweet, *James McNeil Whistler,* Art Institute of Chicago, 1968, 87).

This sketch presents an image of striking freshness and vividness. Apparently rapidly painted, it captures a fleeting moment in which mood is as important a part of this adolescent portrait as it is in the nocturnes. But the note of pathos that Sweet noticed in the National Gallery of Canada's version of this same subject is missing.

KCB

Frank Duveneck   1848–1919

95   *Study of a Woman's Head,* ca. 1875

Oil on canvas, 13 x 8½ inches

Provenance: Theodore Wendell; Fogg Art Museum, Harvard University, Purchase of the Louise E. Bettens Fund (1943.30).

This broad sketch by Frank Duveneck, the most influential American member of the Munich School, has traditionally been identified as a study of Isabella Stewart Gardner. It was probably made about the time of Duveneck's successful show of his early portraits in Boston in 1875, two years after his return from Europe. Its similarity in style to the *Lady with a Fan* of 1873 (Museum of Fine Arts, Boston) further indicates a date from the mid-1870's. Duveneck gave the sketch to his close friend Ted Wendell, a Boston resident, who was among the students following him from Germany to Italy.

The unfinished quality of this study suggests that it was painted in a single sitting and makes the definite identification of the sitter less than totally certain. The painting, however, displays two qualities central to Duveneck's art: a virtuosity of brush work and a restricted palette that emphasizes earth tones.

KCB

Frank Duveneck   1848–1919

96   *Charles William Eliot,* ca. 1893

Marble, height 31¼ inches

Signed on back: Frank Duveneck

Provenance: Harvard University Portrait Collection, Gift of the Class of 1831 through Francis Boott (S 85).

Bibliography: W. Simple, *Exhibition of the Works of Frank Duveneck,* Cincinnati Art Museum, 1936, 12.

Duveneck's sculpture was limited to three pieces: this bust of Charles William Eliot, a life-size statue of Ralph Waldo Emerson, and a memorial to the sculptor's wife in Florence. Harvard is fortunate in owning the first two of the three works. Hidden away for many years, perhaps because of the sitter's displeasure with the likeness, the bust does not display the idealized character projection typical of turn-of-the-century portraiture. The bust is achieved with a high degree of realism, although the modeling of the face is less than inspired. All three pieces of sculpture were achieved in collaboration with Clement J. Barnhorn, a sculptor well known in Duveneck's Cincinnati. Francis Boott, through whom the commission was arranged, was the artist's father-in-law, as well as a close friend of Longfellow, Lowell, and Charles E. Norton.
KCB

George Inness 1825–1894

97 *Durham, Connecticut,* 1869

Oil on panel, 9 x 11¾ inches

Signed in monogram and dated lower right: G.I. 1869

Provenance: Allston Burr; Fogg Art Museum, Harvard University, Bequest of Allston Burr (1949.127).

Bibliography: L. R. Ireland, *The Works of George Inness: An Illustrated Catalogue Raisonné,* Austin, Texas, 1965, no. 460; H. Cikovsky, Jr., *George Inness,* New York, 1971, fig. 40.

Inness painted many views of Durham, Connecticut, the largest number of which date from 1869 and 1879. *Durham, Connecticut* dates from the earlier series and has as its subject the same farm portrayed in *Durham Valley* (Ireland, *Inness,* no. 456). Harvard's landscape was painted prior to Inness' trip to Europe in 1870, but after his conversion to the philosophy of Swedenborg in 1865 and his election to the National Academy in 1868.

Durham, Connecticut is characterized by the thick impasto of Inness' early style and has as its subject a lyrical landscape with a dramatically lit sky which reveals intimations of his religious conviction. This concern with the effects of light is traditional to American landscape painting, but the intimacy of scale, the limited palette, and the generalized details of nature mark Inness' break from the strict representational style of the Hudson River School. In contrast to the larger and more polished works common to the period, this work symbolizes the importance of small works, which best reveal the nineteenth-century artist's virtuosity.

KCB

George Inness

98 *October Noon,* 1891

Oil on canvas, 29½ x 44 inches

Signed and dated lower left: G. Inness 1891

Provenance: Grenville L. Winthrop; Fogg Art Museum, Harvard University, Bequest of Grenville L. Winthrop (1943.137).

Bibliography: L. R. Ireland, *The Works of George Inness: An Illustrated Catalogue Raisonné,* Austin, Texas, 1965, no. 1359; N. Cikovsky, Jr., *George Inness,* New York, 1971, pl. IX.

October Noon represents the best of Inness' late style. It was painted three years before his death, during the period in which he traveled to Florida, California, and New Brunswick. Although the landscape is believable, it is probably an idealized invention of the artist which cannot be related to a specific location. The qualities of peace and prosperity depicted in this landscape are reminiscent of his earlier work, but Inness has gone beyond the influence of the Barbizon School, whose style he had found meaningful and expressive of his view of nature. The painting illustrates the artist's sensitivity to light and tonal movements. The color has a glowing quality which was achieved by glazing rather than the heavy impasto technique of the 1870's. The landscape is also marked by an economy of brushwork and a highly formal composition. By employing shapes which imply the substance of nature with a minimum of detail, Inness has achieved a synthesis of reality and abstraction.

KCB

Thomas Moran 1832–1926

99 *Shoshone Tepee,* ca. 1890

Watercolor and pencil on paper, 7½ x 5⅜ inches

Inscribed lower left: Shoshone

Provenance: The artist to William Holmes; to George Ives Bushnell, 1927; Peabody Museum, Harvard University, Bushnell Collection (41-72-10/444).

In 1871 Moran began what was to be a series of western trips as an artist for the F. V. Hayden government exploring expedition to the Yellowstone Valley. The photographer for the expedition, William H. Jackson, remembered Moran as having "never ridden a horse before and while getting accustomed to this experience, was quite unabashed in using his camp pillow to protect his rather spare anatomy from the hard lines of a McClellan saddle" (W. H. Jackson, "With Moran in the Yellowstone," reprinted from *Appalachia,* Sept. 1938, in Fritiof Fryzell, ed., *Thomas Moran,* East Hampton, New York, 1858, 53-54.) Undaunted, Moran returned many times to the West and finally settled in California in 1916. Although Moran is best remembered for his vast painted panoramas of western scenery, *Shoshone Tepee* indicates the artist's interest in the smaller and less dramatic aspects of Indian life.

An undated letter from Moran to William Holmes suggests that the drawing may have been commissioned by the latter: "My dear Holmes: . . . I have just returned home from the West. I am not settled down to work. Have finished two of the drawings for you and will send them in a day or two. I am indeed 'awfully' busy. . . . I have now over a hundred drawings to make for various parties" (Letter from T. Moran to W. Holmes, undated, Peabody Museum).

NHS

Winslow Homer 1836–1910

100 *Gloucester Harbor with Dory,* 1880

Watercolor, 13¼ x 19 inches

Signed lower right: Winslow Homer

Provenance: Chapin Collection; Osgood Collection; Fogg Art Museum, Harvard University, Anonymous Gift (1939.240).

101 *Schooner at Sunset,* 1880

Watercolor, 9¾ x 13¾ inches

Signed and dated lower right: Homer 1880

Provenance: Mrs. Charles S. Homer; Grenville L. Winthrop; Fogg Art Museum, Harvard University, Bequest of Grenville L. Winthrop (1943.298).

102 *Sailboat and Fourth of July Fireworks,* 1880

Watercolor, 10 x 14 inches

Signed lower right: WH

Dated lower left: July 4, 1880

Provenance: Grenville L. Winthrop; Fogg Art Museum, Harvard University, Bequest of Grenville L. Winthrop (1943.305).

103 *Fishing in the Adirondacks,* ca. 1890

Watercolor, 13⅝ x 19½ inches

Provenance: Fogg Art Museum, Harvard University, Purchase of the Louise E. Bettens Fund (1918.35).

Bibliography: J. Fosburgh, *Winslow Homer in the Adirondacks,* Adirondacks Museum, Blue Mountain Lake, New York, 1959, 47, fig. 19.

104 *The Mink Pond,* 1891

Watercolor, 13⅞ x 20 inches

Signed and dated lower right: Mink Pond, 1891/Winslow Homer

Provenance: Grenville L. Winthrop; Fogg Art Museum, Harvard University, Bequest of Grenville L. Winthrop (1943.304).

Bibliography: L. Goodrich, *Winslow Homer,* New York, 1944, 117; J. T. Flexner, *The World of Winslow Homer 1836–1910,* New York, 1966, 129.

105 *Hunter in the Adirondacks,* 1892

Watercolor, 13¼ x 19½ inches

Signed and dated lower right: 1892 Homer

Provenance: Chapin Collection; Osgood Collection; Grenville L. Winthrop; Fogg Art Museum, Harvard University, Bequest of Grenville L. Winthrop (1939.230).

Bibliography: L. Goodrich, *Winslow Homer,* New York, 1944, fig. 32; J. W. Fosburgh, *Winslow Homer in the Adirondacks* [exhibition catalogue], Adirondacks Museum, Blue Mountain Lake, New York, 1959, 74, fig. 46.

106   *Adirondack Lake* or *Blue Monday No. 16,* 1892

Watercolor, 12 x 21⅛ inches

Signed and dated lower right: Winslow Homer, 1892

Provenance: Goelet Gallatin; Grenville L. Winthrop; Fogg Art Museum, Harvard University, Bequest of Grenville L. Winthrop (1943.302).

Bibliography: J. W. Fosburgh, *Winslow Homer in the Adirondacks* [exhibition catalogue], Adirondacks Museum, Blue Mountain Lake, New York, 1959, 75, fig. 47.

107   *Homosassa Jungle in Florida,* 1904

Watercolor, 14 x 22 inches

Signed and dated lower left: Homer 1904

Provenance: Charles S. Homer; Fogg Art Museum, Harvard University, Gift of Mrs. Charles S. Homer in memory of the late Charles Homer and his brother Winslow Homer (1935.50).

The Fogg collection of Homer watercolors is representative of the artist's entire development. The best of the collection are works of the Gloucester and Adirondacks subjects.

Gloucester provided Homer with material for many watercolors and oils, of which perhaps the most famous is *Breezing Up* from 1876. The three Gloucester watercolors date from 1880, also the year in which Homer began to be mentioned frequently in the newspapers. *Gloucester Harbor with Dory* contains the theme of a boy perched on the bow of a dory and displays Homer's suspension of time and age within a world in harmony. The sharpness of the contrasts and the force of the foreground image illustrate Downes' statement that from 1880 onward Homer had the faculty for making striking and original pictorial design (W. Downes, *Winslow Homer,* New York, 1911, 96), although the work still contains traces of underlying drawing.

Schooner at Sunset begins to display a sustained mastery over the watercolor medium, although there is still visible some of that underlying drawing which was so important to earlier watercolors and which took the edge

off the quality of spontaneity. This example has a simple composition, and its compelling effect is made by its bright color and technical mastery of wet and dry washes to achieve sparkling light.

Sailboat and Fourth of July Fireworks stands as a singular experiment in the development of Homer's watercolor technique. Unlike the other two examples from the Gloucester period, there is little evidence of underlying drawing. The emphasis is on reproducing the color and the visual effects of fireworks at night. There are no hard edges, and the wet technique comes closer to approximating in watercolor a French Impressionist image than does the *Houses of Parliament* (Joseph H. Hirshhorn Collection) painted the following year on a trip to England, which is directly parallel to Monet in color and subject. These three watercolors reveal Homer's technical development at a crucial period. It was not until later that Homer was able to inject a deeper meaning into his paintings of the sea.

Homer made numerous trips to the Adirondacks between 1870 and 1904. His Adirondacks phase of the 1890's was a new and original departure in the American tradition of watercolor. Having attained technical mastery, Homer was able to treat his subject matter with a new brilliance and a depth of feeling missing in his work of the 1870's. Instead of detailing all elements equally, he was able to paint essentials and simplify the incidental, thus increasing his impact. Homer experienced a growing popularity marked in 1890 by an exhibition of thirty-two Adirondacks watercolors at Doll and Richards in Boston.

Fishing was one of Homer's great delights, and the Adirondacks experience served him both as a period of refreshment and as a source of inspiration for pictures like *Fishing in the Adirondacks* of 1890 and the outstanding *Blue Monday No. 16* of 1892. These two watercolors illustrate Homer's ability, in his midfifties, to exploit fully the spontaneous and transparent nature of the medium. In both examples he minimizes details, and although he uses a wide range of tones, it is the blues which prevail. In *Blue Monday No. 16* Homer's restrained use of a sparkling white light not only gives resonance to the deep blue tones, but also defines the clarity of the atmosphere. Homer's ability to reproduce the quality of light reflecting on the water and flashing off

the fishing rod extends the feeling of time beyond the moment represented. As Goodrich states, "In these watercolors he was reaching the climax of his art."

Mink Pond is a life-size close-up of small creatures isolated from the larger world. Devoid of human presence, it reveals Homer's love of and communion with nature. Unlike a photograph which unnaturally stops action, this watercolor captures the image of an atmosphere in tension, as if the butterfly were hovering and the fish were still for a moment, instinctively sensing some unspecified danger. In this example Homer is able to imply the potential for movement and the charged atmosphere inherent in the subject. In many ways, this work recalls a sensibility similar to that of La Farge (see No. 79) in his watercolors of water lilies. The delicacy of touch, the formality of the composition, and the sensitivity to color caused Flexner to remark that the painting exudes "an oriental air" (Flexner, *Homer*, 129).

Perhaps the most famous work by Homer at the Fogg Museum is the *Hunter in the Adirondacks,* which most clearly deals with his continual theme of man in his environment. This picture reveals supremely well Homer's understanding of man's spiritual need for nature. As in most of the Adirondacks watercolors, the dominant mood is one of stillness and solitude, and the theme of hunting seems incidental to the larger theme of man's oneness with nature. This watercolor is important for a number of reasons. The composition is marked by a formal concern with pattern in the front plane, and there is an unusual emphasis on the handling of detail. This is in contrast to such works as *Adirondack Lake,* in which only the most important elements are detailed and a greater romantic feeling is projected. In addition, this watercolor contains a recognizable portrait of Mike "Farmer" Flynn, the model for the young man in his Adirondacks pictures (Wiley Gatchell was his counterpart in those at Prout's Neck). It is interesting to note that Homer was able to portray the specific features of his subjects, in spite of the small size of the works and the difficulty of the medium.

Early in 1904, at the age of sixty-eight, Homer made a trip to Homosassa Springs where the bass fishing was reputed to be the best in America. This spot sixty miles north of Tampa was the inspiration for some of his freest improvisations in watercolor. The theme of a solitary fisherman in *Homosassa Jungle in Florida* is the same as that of the Adirondack series. The figure of the old man is probably a transposition of "Old Mountain Phelps," the figure in the Adirondacks pictures, rather than a person actually seen in Florida. The bright light and color are specific to Florida and add to the impression of exuberance which Homer imparted to this series late in his career.

KCB

Homer D. Martin 1836–1897

108 *Blossoming Trees,* ca. 1881–1886

Oil on panel, 15 x 24 inches

Provenance: Mrs. Charles O. Gates; Dr. F. L. Babbott; Grenville L. Winthrop; Fogg Art Museum, Harvard University, Bequest of Grenville L. Winthrop (1943.140).

Bibliography: E. G. Martin, *Homer Martin, A Reminiscence,* New York, 1904, fig. 24; H. Dana, *Fifty-eight Paintings by Homer D. Martin,* New York, 1913, fig. 25.

109 *English Channel,* 1885

Oil on canvas, 14½ x 23¼ inches

Signed and dated lower right: H. D. Martin 85

Provenance: Mariana G. Van Renssalaer; Fogg Art Museum, Harvard University, Bequest of Mariana G. Van Renssalaer (1934.120).

Homer Martin received some training in Albany from James Hart, but from the first he admired J. C. Corot, and it is not surprising that on his first trip abroad in 1876 he should visit Barbizon. He maintained a New York studio in the 10th Street Building from 1864 until 1881, when he returned to Europe. While abroad he became a friend of J. A. M. Whistler (see Nos. 92–94) in England, and after a visit to Pennedepie in 1881 he settled in Villerville and Honfleur between 1882 and 1886.

During this European period Martin apparently completed few finished oil paintings, but instead made sketches for works like the *Harp of the Winds* (Metropolitan Museum of Art) which was painted after his return to the United States. *English Channel,* 1885, is an example of these sketches. Martin had become fond of the watercolor medium at this time, as made evident by the delicacy of touch in this example. This work displays a different style of painting from that of his great Adirondacks pictures of the 1870's. The formality of the composition reflects the influence of Whistler. The lighthouse in this work differs in detail and background from Martin's frequent representations of the one at Honfleur (see F. J. Mather, *Homer Martin,* New York, 1912, 64).

Blossoming Trees is a colorful and intimate study of a fragile moment in nature. Unlike Martin's many landscapes which project feelings of austerity and remoteness, this work reveals a joyous spirit. It also displays Martin's impressionist style of applying paint in parallel strokes sometimes flattened with a palette knife to achieve a shimmering effect of color and atmosphere. It is impossible to date this picture more accurately than the spring of a year between 1881 and 1886.

KCB

Augustus Saint-Gaudens 1848–1907

110 *Standing Lincoln with Chair,* 1885

Bronze, height 40¾ inches

Provenance: Grenville L. Winthrop; Fogg Art Museum, Harvard University, Bequest of Grenville L. Winthrop (1943.1116).

Bibliography: C. L. Hind, *Augustus Saint-Gaudens,* New York, 1908, 303; W. Craven, *Sculpture in America,* New York, 1968, 384; L. Tharp, *Saint-Gaudens and the Gilded Era,* Boston, 1969, 208.

111 *Robert Louis Stevenson,* 1887

Bronze, height 17⅝ inches

Provenance: Houghton Library, Harvard University.

Bibliography: Carnegie Institute, *Augustus Saint-Gaudens Memorial Exhibition,* Pittsburgh, 1909, 49; L. Tharp, *Saint-Gaudens and the Gilded Era,* Boston, 1969, 211.

Saint-Gaudens was born the son of a French shoemaker in Dublin, Ireland, and was apprenticed at the age of thirteen to a New York cameo cutter. He studied at the Cooper Union and at the National Academy of Design. From 1867 to 1875 he was primarily in Europe and studied for a time at the Academie des Beaux Arts. In 1880 he settled in New York, where in 1885 he completed the *Standing Lincoln* which was installed two years later in Chicago's Lincoln Park. The sculptor copyrighted many replicas which were sold at Tiffany's in New York for two thousand dollars each (Hind, *Saint-Gaudens,* 303) and at Doll and Richards in Boston. The Fogg version is one of the replicas.

Saint-Gaudens' use of bronze instead of marble was new for American sculpture and underscored the shift away from the Roman ideal. The sculptor's reference to plaster casts of Lincoln's face and hands as models emphasizes his role in leading American sculpture away from the neoclassic tradition of Powers toward a greater realism. His was not, however, the explicit realism of the Rogers groups (see No. 70), for *Lincoln* expresses the qualities of dignity, strength, and courage that became the standard ideal for the representation of the great emancipator. Saint-Gaudens' ability to pose the subject in a memorable position endowed the statue with recognizable human qualities. The sculptor had the special ability to balance the realism of the details with the idealism inherent in the subject.

The *Robert Louis Stevenson* bas-relief best displays Saint-Gaudens' sensitive and restrained mode of portrait representation. This form of sculpture was probably influenced by his training as a cameo cutter, combining his French discipline and American penchant for realism. The sittings for the head and shoulders took place in a New York hotel while Stevenson was ill, and the studies for the hands were made at Manasquan just before Stevenson left for Samoa in 1887. This particular example is a copyrighted electrotype reduction of the type sold at Tiffany's in two sizes.

Restraint characterizes both the *Standing Lincoln with Chair* and the *Stevenson* bas-relief. Lincoln appears in an attitude of introspection; Stevenson stares straight ahead. In both cases Saint-Gaudens introduces elements which balance the actual with the ideal. The chair symbolizes the power of Lincoln's office in contrast with his human qualities, while the blanket over Stevenson's knees points to the man's frail health in contrast to his powers of imagination. Although the details are precisely represented, the freedom from unnecessary detail and the sensitivity to meaningful gesture elevate Saint-Gaudens above the majority of nineteenth-century American sculptors.

KCB

John H. Twachtman 1853–1902

112 *Landscape,* 1888

Oil on panel, 12¼ x 14¾ inches

Provenance: William S. Monroe; Fogg Art Museum, Harvard University, Bequest of William S. Monroe (1927.228).

Twachtman was a member of the "Ten," the American impressionist movement in the early 1890's, which included J. A. Weir, Hassam, Simmons, Tarbell, DeCamp, Reid, Benson, Dewing, and Metcalf. He began his development in the mid-1870's when he was with Duveneck and Chase in Munich. In 1883, when he worked at the Academie Julien, his style changed to a low-key, limited palette, with an emphasis on pattern and an elimination of bravura brushwork. During this French phase he painted at Honfleur, as did Homer Martin (Nos. 108-109). His best-known work came from his Greenwich phase and includes the Horseneck Falls series and the commissioned Niagara and Yellowstone subjects.

Landscape duplicates the composition of the High Museum's *Along the River, Winter,* 1899 (R. Boyle, *John Henry Twachtman, a Retrospective Exhibition,* Cincinnati Art Museum, 1966), at the beginning of the Greenwich phase. However, the former recalls fall rather than winter; the mood is threatening and dark in contrast to the brightness of the other. The comparison of these paintings reveals Twachtman's ability to evoke the subtle moods caused by the changes in nature, as well as his evident concern with the act of painting. The inspiration of J. A. M. Whistler (see Nos. 92-94) after 1883 explains in part Twachtman's formal approach to composition, simplification of elements, close harmony of colors, and careful brushwork.

KCB

Thomas Eakins   1844–1916

113   *Portrait of a Young Woman, Miss Alice Kurtz,*
       1903

Oil on canvas, 23⅝ x 19¼ inches

Signed lower right: Eakins

Provenance: Miss Alice B. Kurtz (Mrs. John B. Whiteman); Fogg Art Museum, Harvard University, Presented by John Coolidge, Director of the Fogg Museum, Funds for this acquisition were contributed by his many friends (1969.1).

Bibliography: L. Goodrich, *Thomas Eakins: His Life and Works,* New York, 1933, no. 379; S. Schendler, *Eakins,* Boston, 1967, no. 143, 265.

Painted in 1903, *Portrait of a Young Woman* is a step in the development of such works as the *Portrait of Mrs. Edith Mahon* (Smith College Museum of Art) from Eakins' most profound period. Although he had remained independent from the mainstream of financially successful artists like Sargent, the early 1900's brought Eakins growing recognition. Following a portrait of Alice Kurtz's father made the same summer, this picture represents a format which Eakins developed in the period of 1902–1904. The head and shoulders of the young woman in an attitude of reverie reveal Eakins' preoccupation with the individual in isolation, unencumbered by props or even the element of hands. Unconcerned with charm or beauty, the painting strives to reveal insights into self-awareness, frailty, physical endurance, and will. The brown tonality and depth of perception display Eakins' interest in the work of Velasquez. The harshness of the light, which gives the skin a gritty quality, fails to enliven the dress material and testifies to the artist's single-minded pursuit of psychological insight.

KCB

Bela Lyon Pratt 1867–1917

114 *The Bather,* 1904

Marble, height 16½ inches

Signed and dated on base: B. L. Pratt 1904

Provenance: Dr. Arthur T. Cabot; Fogg Art Museum, Harvard University, Bequest of Dr. Arthur T. Cabot (1939.308).

Pratt studied at the Yale School of Fine Arts at the age of sixteen and later at the Art Students League in New York. He also worked as an assistant in Saint-Gaudens' studio. In 1890 he went to the Academie des Beaux Arts in Paris. Upon his return to the United States in 1892 he began to teach modeling at the Museum of Fine Arts in Boston. His sculpture for the Columbian Exposition of 1893 established his reputation, which led to the two muses in front of the Boston Public Library, and several busts commissioned by Harvard, of which the *Phillips Brooks* of 1899 and the *Colonel Henry Lee* of 1902 are among the best. The small-scale *Bather* is particularly interesting because it is not a portrait. Meant for private rather than public appreciation, it represents the artist's personal sensibility. Like all of Pratt's marble sculpture, the *Bather* is marked by an impression of softness. The sugary surface texture gives the figure warmth, and the simplification of details and blurring of edges help to create the turn-of-the-century's vision of pure maidenhood.

KCB

John Singer Sargent 1856–1925

115 *The Musicians* (Study for *El Jaleo*), ca. 1879

Oil on canvas, 23¾ x 31¼ inches

Provenance: Grenville L. Winthrop; Fogg Art Museum, Harvard University, Bequest of Grenville L. Winthrop (1943.153).

Bibliography: R. Ormond, *John Singer Sargent, Painting, Drawings, Watercolors,* New York, 1970, 28.

116 *The Breakfast Table,* 1884

Oil on canvas, 21¾ x 18¼ inches

Inscribed and signed lower right: à mon cher ami Besnard/John S. Sargent

Provenance: Miss Anna R. Mills; Grenville L. Winthrop; Fogg Art Museum, Harvard University, Bequest of Grenville L. Winthrop (1943.150).

Bibliography: M. Birnbaum, *John Singer Sargent,* New York, 1941, 29; D. McKibbin, *Sargent's Boston* [exhibition catalogue], Museum of Fine Arts, Boston, 1956, 22, fig. 8; R. Ormond, *John Singer Sargent, Painting, Drawings, Watercolors,* New York, 1970, 31, fig. 32.

117 *Sebastino* or *Man Reading,* ca. 1910

Watercolor, 13⅝ x 20¾ inches

Signed lower right: John S. Sargent

Provenance: Grenville L. Winthrop; Fogg Art Museum, Harvard University, Bequest of Grenville L. Winthrop (1943.315).

Bibliography: M. Birnbaum, *John Singer Sargent,* New York, 1941, 59, fig. 11; D. McKibbin, *Sargent's Boston* [exhibition catalogue], Museum of Fine Arts, Boston, 1956, 92.

118 *In the Tyrol,* ca. 1911

Watercolor, 14 x 19¾ inches

Signed upper right: John S. Sargent

Provenance: Hon. Evan Charteris K. C.; Sir Joseph Duveen; Fogg Art Museum, Harvard University, Gift of Sir Joseph Duveen (1927.7).

119 *Lake O'Hara,* 1916

Oil on canvas, 37½ x 44 inches

Signed and dated lower left: John S. Sargent, 1916

Provenance: Fogg Art Museum, Harvard University, Purchase of the Louise E. Bettens Fund (1916.496).

Bibliography: W. H. Downes, *John S. Sargent, His Life and Works,* Boston, 1925, 248; R. Ormond, *John Singer Sargent, Painting, Drawings, Watercolors,* New York, 1970, 78.

120 *Classical Urn,* 1918

Watercolor, 20 x 16 inches

Dated lower right: M. de[?] 1918

Provenance: Grenville L. Winthrop; Fogg Art Museum, Harvard University, Bequest of Grenville L. Winthrop (1943.318).

The Harvard Collection is extremely rich in works by Sargent, and this exhibition includes examples covering the span of his career. Earliest is *The Musicians,* one of several studies for *El Jaleo* (Isabella S. Gardner Museum, Boston), the large exhibition piece which was a success at the Salon of 1882. *El Jaleo* was entirely a studio production, although it is said to have been inspired by dancers whom Sargent sketched in Spain during 1879. Whether this work is one of the original sketches is conjectural. It is known, however, that Kenyon Cox was the model for the hands of the guitarist in the final painting. The bright colors, diminished in the final version, and the unfinished nature of the sketch with its controlled brushwork might indicate that this was one of the original studies.

The Breakfast Table was probably painted at the beginning of 1884 during Sargent's family visit in Nice. A photograph exists of the completed painting on an easel in his Paris studio (McKibbin, *Sargent's Boston,* fig. 7). The painting represents Sargent's sister Violet (later Mrs. Ormond) at breakfast and includes a sparkling still life with silver objects in the foreground. Intimate in scale and brilliantly colored, the work displays Sargent's gift for the portraiture of woman. He painted a similar subject, *A Dinner Table at Night (the Glass of Claret)* (David Pleydell-Bouverie, California) early in the summer of 1884 when he visited Lavington Rectory near Petworth, and another in 1885 of the Besnard family called *Fête Familliale* (Minneapolis Institute of Art). *The Breakfast Table,* while using similar devices, seems more surely handled and less theatrically staged.

Watercolor became Sargent's favorite medium after 1900, and the majority of his huge output was produced for his own pleasure. *Sebastino,* originally entitled *Nicola Reading* (Birnbaum, *Sargent,* 59), is a portrait of Nicola D'Inverno, Sargent's personal servant after 1892. Both the subject of a man on a bed and the objects on the table in this picture resemble those in a watercolor of L. A. Harrison entitled *Asleep* (Miss Sylvia Harrison, Portofino). McKibbin dates the Sargent watercolor from 1910, although *Asleep* is dated 1900. Sebastino is similar in its technical virtuosity, brown coloring, and use of the white of the paper to Sargent's splendid Majorca horse subjects of 1909. The various tones in the mountain of pillows were a natural theme for watercolor, and Sargent exploited their possibilities in a number of pictures.

Sargent spent the summers of 1908–1909 and 1911–1913 at Purtud in the Simplon, where his sister Violet Ormond and her family joined him regularly. His nieces and their friends, the Barnard girls, served as models for his many pictures of groups of women with billowing pale dresses and parasols. *In the Tyrol,* probably dating from 1911, is a well-known example of this genre. The delineation is done with a brush. He achieves with singular virtuosity the effect of bright sunlight.

In 1916, after completing his work on the Boston Public Library, Sargent, in the tradition of Alpine holidays, took a two-month camping trip into the Canadian Rockies during which he produced some of his best watercolors and the two oils *Lake O'Hara* and *Yoho Falls* (Isabella S. Gardner Museum, Boston). Altogether unlike his Alpine works, these landscapes have a new flavor, accurately capturing with bravura brushwork the light and color of the West. The extreme visibility of the brush strokes gives *Lake O'Hara* a feeling of superficiality which counteracts somewhat the beauty of the scene and the richness of the color. *Lake O'Hara* stands as a remarkable work outside the mainstream of his late subject matter, in the same way that *The Breakfast Table* does from his best early period.

Classical Urn is the latest work by Sargent represented here. Its technical virtuosity and rich color give the image compelling attraction at first view. It was painted perhaps at Boulogne when Sargent was an official artist for the Imperial War Museum. In this same year, at Arras, he produced in oil *Ruined Cathedral,* which displays a similar interest in architectural ornament, light, and color. Few of his works during this period show a concern for the war; "Sargent himself admitted that he was fiddling while Rome burnt" (Ormond, *Sargent,* 18).

KCB

Charles Humphriss 1867-?

121 *Appeal to Manito,* 1906

Bronze, height 30½ inches

Signed and dated on base: Ch. Humphriss 1906

Provenance: Lewis K. Sillcox; Graduate School of Business Administration, Harvard University, Gift of Lewis K. Sillcox, 1954.

Little is known about Humphriss except that he was born in England in 1867 and worked in New York, where he was a member of the National Association of Sculptors. *Appeal to Manito* is one of his three known works, the others being *Indians Appeal to Manito* and *Indian Sun Dial.* Indian subject matter was traditional to American sculpture throughout the nineteenth cenury. The turn of the century witnessed a revival of concern with the Indian, once the West had been tamed. *Appeal to Manito* represents the Indian more realistically in style and content than had earlier statues such as Bartlett's *Bohemian Bear Tamer* (Metropolitan Museum of Art). The theme of an appeal to the Indian god Manito was made famous in an equestrian statue by Cyrus Dallin (Museum of Fine Arts, Boston).

KCB

Childe Hassam 1859–1935

122 *Headlands,* 1908

Oil on canvas, 24¼ x 29¼ inches

Signed and dated lower right: Childe Hassam 1908.

Inscribed on back: Headlands/CH [monogram within circle]/1908

Provenance: Archer M. Huntington; Fogg Art Museum, Harvard University, Gift of Archer M. Huntington (1936.131).

Childe Hassam is the best known of the American Impressionists. His method of juxtaposing strokes of clear color to create a vivid expression of light and its effects seem closest to that of his French counterparts. He believed, however, that the origins of Impressionism were English rather than French. In 1886, at the age of twenty-seven, he went to Paris where he spent three years. In 1898 he was a founding member of the "Ten." His vision was essentially American in color and in choice of New England subject matter, which includes scenes from Old Lyme, Cos Cob, Gloucester, and Appledore (Isles of the Shoals).

Painted in 1908, *Headlands* offers a contrast to the series of urban flag pictures which Hassam started in the same year. It represents a view of the New Hampshire island of Appledore, which the artist visited with his friend Celia Thaxter.

KCB

Charles Schreyvogel 1861–1912

123 *The Last Drop,* 1908

Bronze, height 11½ inches

Signed and dated: Copyright 1908 — Charles Schreyvogel

Provenance: Lewis K. Sillcox; Graduate School of Business Administration, Harvard University, Gift of Lewis K. Sillcox, 1954.

Bibliography: R. Taft, *Artists and Illustrators of the Old West 1850-1900,* New York, 1953, 231.

Schreyvogel, who studied in Munich in 1887, was, like Remington and Russell, a sculptor as well as a painter. His greatest period of productivity was in 1900, and his work was concerned with the rememberance of a passing life style on the frontier, depending on the study of written records and costumes for details. Apparently his primary compositions were worked out in clay models. *The Last Drop* and *White Eagle* (an Indian chief) were two popular examples cast in bronze and sold at Tiffany's. After 1909, in the period between Remington and Russell, Schreyvogel was regarded as the leading painter of Western themes.

KCB

Daniel Chester French 1850–1931

124 *Spirit of the Waters,* 1914

Bronze, height 32½ inches

Signed and dated on base: D. C. French Sc. 1914

Provenance: Mrs. Paul Fitz Simons; Grenville L. Winthrop; Fogg Art Museum, Harvard University, Bequest of Grenville L. Winthrop (1943.1361).

Bibliography: M. F. Cresson, *Daniel Chester French,* American Sculptor's Series, New York, 1922.

125 *Lincoln Seated,* 1916

Bronze, height 32 inches

Signed and dated on side of base: D. C. French, March 1916

Provenance: Grenville L. Winthrop; Fogg Art Museum, Harvard University, Bequest of Grenville L. Winthrop (1943.1108).

Bibliography: M. F. Cresson, *Journey Into Fame,* Cambridge, Mass., 1947, 270-281.

French's work epitomizes the ideal imagery of the late nineteenth century in which abstract concepts were personified in the figures of youths and maidens. He studied anatomy with William Rimmer (see Nos. 77-78) in Boston and with J. Q. Ward in New York. Rather than going to Paris with the rest of his generation, however, he went to Florence to study under Thomas Ball. His reputation began in 1874 with his statue of the *Minute Man* in Lexington, Massachusetts. His major works aimed at representing the high ideals and aspirations of the major cultural institutions being given architectural form during his lifetime. His large statue of *John Harvard* in Harvard Yard is a restrained example of this kind of sculpture.

Spirit of the Waters dates from the period of World War I, which provided French with more commissions for memorials than he could fill. The fountain figure is smaller and more personal than his larger memorials for schools and towns. Its idealization of features, simplification of details, and projection of mood cloak the sensual content of the figure.

Lincoln Seated, a study for the Lincoln Memorial in Washington, D. C., is regarded as the peak of his career. French worked on this project from 1915 until 1918. The final marble statue was completed in 1922 by members of the Piccirrilli family of New York. The Fogg's example is a cast of one of the three-foot versions which preceeded the final eight-foot model. French owed a large debt to the two versions of Lincoln by Saint-Gaudens (see No. 110). Both sculptors worked from the casts of Lincoln's face and hands in the Smithsonian Institution. In its idealized qualities, size, and setting, the Lincoln Memorial remains the final word in making palpable the Lincoln myth.

KCB

F. Maxfield Parrish 1870–1966

126 *Illustration for "Baa Baa Black Sheep Have You Any Wool"*

Lithographic crayon and india ink on white paper, 13⅜ x 11¼ inches

Provenance: Charles Bain Hoyt; Fogg Art Museum, Harvard University, Gift of Charles Bain Hoyt, Esq. (1934.181).

Bibliography: *Christian Science Monitor,* April 1945.

F. Maxfield Parrish, the son of the painter Stephen Parrish, was born into and immediately submerged in the entire tradition of Western art. At the age of seven he had already viewed the Louvre's galleries and the Gobelin tapestry works. This background does not necessarily produce an artist of towering stature, but it assured him from blundering into the commonplace.

Parrish's world is one of blissful yet somewhat threatening surrealism, a dream world of successive intimate and secret places. His colors and deployment of shape hint that he is also a logical forebear to the current vogue for the soft mists of the lyrical colorists.

This particular drawing was produced to illustrate *Mother Goose in Prose,* published in Chicago in 1897 and written by L. Frank Baum (the author of *The Wizard of Oz*). This book launched Parrish's career as an illustrator, and his influence in this field has been felt into the present day.

HZR

John Gutzon Borglum   1867–1941

127   *Head of a Woman*

Marble, height 13⅜ inches

Signed on side: Gutzon Borglum

Provenance: Mr. and Mrs. Robert Woods Bliss; Dumbarton Oaks Research Library and Collection; Fogg Art Museum, Harvard University (1942.154).

Borglum studied in California with the painter William Keith and in Paris at the Academie Julien. He achieved fame with his *Mares of Diomedes* (Metropolitan Museum of Art), whose skillful portrayal of horses subsequently earned him the commission for the *Statue of Sheridan* at Sheridan Circle in Washington, D. C. His work includes a huge *Head of Lincoln* at the Capitol, many sculptures in the Cathedral of St. John the Divine in New York, and the colossal series of Presidential Heads on Mt. Rushmore in South Dakota. *Head of a Woman* reflects a more private sensibility than the colossal sculptures for which he is remembered today. Possibly it dates from around 1905, when Borglum was working on St. John the Divine and was forced to replace his heads of angels because they looked too much like women.

KCB

Robert Henri 1865–1929

128 *Portrait of Eakers,* 1904

Oil on canvas, 29¼ x 23¼ inches (sight)

Inscribed upper right: To my friend Eakers 1904

Provenance: Castano Gallery, Boston; Fogg Art Museum, Harvard University, Purchase of the Louise E. Bettens Fund (1948.85).

Robert Henry Cozad (Robert Henri) studied with Thomas Anshutz starting in 1886 in the Pennsylvania Academy of Fine Arts, and from 1888 to 1891 he was a pupil of both Fleury and Bouguereau at the Academie Julien and the Ecole des Beaux Arts in Paris. Even though he rejected this academic background, Post-Impressionism swirled unheeded around Henri in Paris. He returned to America an apostle of the broadly painterly as he had seen it, first in Velasquez, then Manet; he cared for few of the moderns.

He inculcated this taste for lean and economic means in his pupils — a glowing list of major talents, among them Charles Sheeler (see Nos. 129, 130, 143, 144), Everett Shinn (see No. 131), George Bellows (see Nos. 137-138), Edward Hopper (see No. 146), Patrick Henry Bruce, and Stuart Davis. In 1904, the very year he painted the *Portrait of Eakers,* Henri came to New York to teach at the New York School of Art founded by William Merritt Chase. There he promoted his style of uncompromising and unflattering portraiture. Immediacy and precision in depicting character, without the fussiness of Eakins, whom Henri greatly admired, typify his work of this period.

His students rallying around him formed "The Eight," and with them, Henri their common background and bridge to the past, American art came into the twentieth century.

HZR

Charles Sheeler 1883–1965

129 *Landscape,* 1914

Black crayon on white paper, 5 1/16 x 7 1/4 inches

Signed and dated lower left: Sheeler 1914

Provenance: John Quinn; Charles Bain Hoyt; Fogg Art Museum, Harvard University, Gift of Charles Bain Hoyt (1939.243).

Bibliography: American Art Association, *Paintings and Sculpture: The Renowned Collection of Modern and Ultra-Modern Art Formed by the Late John Quinn,* New York, 1927.

130 *Landscape*

Black crayon on white paper (a page from a sketchbook), 5 7/8 x 6 15/16 inches

Provenance: Charles Bain Hoyt; Fogg Art Museum, Harvard University, Gift of Charles Bain Hoyt (1939.247).

Charles Sheeler was born in Philadelphia in 1883 and traveled to Europe in 1904, 1905, and 1909; he was undoubtedly familiar with the most noteworthy trends in Continental art during that first decade of the twentieth century. In 1913 he exhibited in the Armory Show, and by 1914, as these two drawings show, he had absorbed the examples of Cézanne and Braque, thus putting him at the forefront of American experimenters. For an American, far removed from the centers of Cubism and Fauvism, to have so thoroughly and accurately understood the contributions of early modern art was indeed an achievement.

Eventually the American in him, evidenced by a love of the specific and the objective, took precedence in Sheeler. After these early works he turned his full attention to photography and to painting the clarity of the mechanical world as the repository for the concerns of still life.

HZR

Everett Shinn 1876–1953

131 *Central Park, New York,* 1915

Watercolor and black chalk on paper, 4⅛ x 5¹³⁄₁₆ inches

Dated and signed lower right: E. Shinn 1915

Label on the frame gives the location as being 73rd Street and Central Park West.

Provenance: A gift of the artist to John G. Pierce; Fogg Art Museum, Harvard University, Gift of Mrs. John G. Pierce in memory of her husband (1963.114).

In Everett Shinn we have perhaps the most light-hearted and human member of "The Eight," seeking out the lyrical even in the gaudy spectacle of the music hall. His spontaneous, dancing brushwork and glittering sketches contrast markedly with the decorative yet somber art of his youth, which he once characterized as "an adjunct of plush and cut glass" (E. Shinn, *The Eight,* Brooklyn Museum, 1943).

Trained first in mechanical draughting at the Spring Garden Institute in 1891, Shinn transferred quickly to the Pennsylvania Academy of Fine Arts. Like Sloan, Glackens, and Luks, all members of "The Eight," Shinn was a newspaper illustrator, and from 1896 to 1901 he worked on papers in Philadelphia; from 1897 to 1901 at the time he started to paint seriously, he worked in New York for the *Herald* and the *World*.

One would expect a newspaper man to be hard-boiled and somewhat callous, but Shinn's work has a delicacy that underlines the pathos and transiency of city life: its theaters, spurious gaiety, dispassionate and unresponsive urban spaces. The drawing *Central Park* is the intimate description of a sensitive observer, alone, roaming the city.

HZR

Elie Nadelman 1882–1946

132 *The Pianiste,* ca. 1917

Painted wood (the base is a later addition), height 36 inches

Provenance: Philip L. Goodwin, 1948; John P. Spiegel; Fogg Art Museum, Harvard University, Gift of Dr. and Mrs. John P. Spiegel (1956.200).

Bibliography: L. Kirstein, *Sculpture of Elie Nadelman* [exhibition catalogue], Museum of Modern Art, New York, 1948, 30.

It would be difficult to overestimate the importance of the sculpture of Elie Nadelman. His outwardly bland figures have never gathered the following of other, basically less significant, work. While he was in Europe, Nadelman's influence suffused the highest circles of artistic speculation, and in America (he arrived on the Lusitania on 31 October 1914) he influenced a whole generation of artists.

Nadelman was among the first to understand the worth and personality of native American folk art, and he acquired an enormous collection of folk-craft. This anonymous native tradition intrigued him and was incorporated in his art.

The Pianiste combines a severity of form and limited number of shapes, and yet it is a light, airy work. The witty detail, the woman's hair ribbon and her dress strings, her painted features, eyes slit in a coquettish grin, relieve what would otherwise have been an oppressive massiveness. Two unrelieved forms, the piano's rectangular bulk and the woman's conical shape, would in no way have yielded the result they attain here without Nadelman's refinement of proportions and clever, human details.

HZR

Jo Davidson   1882–1952

133   *Joffre,* 1919

Bronze, 10¼ x 12¼ x 6¾ inches

Inscribed on front: J. Joffre

Inscribed on back: Jo Davidson Paris 1919 (3)

Provenance: Grenville L. Winthrop; Fogg Art Museum, Harvard University, Bequest of Grenville L. Winthrop (1943.1390).

Elegant, though surely lacking conceptual profundity to modern taste, this portrait bust amply captures the rugged ideal of the "great man," the Marshal of the French forces in the First World War. The bust of *Joffre* has fine detail, a rich reddish brown patina, a good sense of spatial presence, if not of psychological depth. Because contemporary taste in sculpture is rooted in ideation and formal manipulation, we seem to have become somewhat used to ignoring, or at least are not quite at ease with, modern occasional and portrait sculpture. When faced with an obviously dedicatory work, modern reflexive art-viewing strategems can be up-ended by an adequate, which is to say, a solid performance.

HZR

Maurice Brazil Prendergast 1859–1924

134 *Beach, New England 1920*

Watercolor over graphite on white paper, 15¼ x 22⅛ inches

Signed lower right: Prendergast

Inscribed on back: Beach, New England 1920

Provenance: Charles Prendergast; Fogg Art Museum, Harvard University, Gift of Mrs. Charles Prendergast (1961.137).

Bibliography: H. Rhys, "Prendergast," *Arts,* 19, no. 4, 1926.

In 1861 Prendergast moved to Boston with his brother Charles, and lived there until the two moved in 1914 to New York, where Maurice died ten years later. Prendergast, the oldest of "The Eight," was neither a student of Henri's nor a journalist; he was not even a realist, but consistently and strongly a Post-Impressionist.

However, Prendergast maintained the company of "The Eight," exhibiting with them in 1908 and again in 1913 at the Armory Show. He combined in his work a very clear penchant for formal organization with a dazzling watercolor technique, relying on tiny open patches of flickering white paper to both heighten the plein-air color and establish the surface of the picture.

HZR

Charles Demuth   1883–1935

135   *Lily,* 1923

Watercolor on white paper, 22⅞ x 17 inches

Signed and dated lower left: C. Demuth 1923

Provenance: Fogg Art Museum, Harvard University, Gift of Friends of the Fogg (1925.5.1).

136   *Fruit and Sunflowers,* ca. 1924

Watercolor on white paper, 17¾ x 11⅞ inches

Unsigned

Provenance: The Daniel Gallery, New York; Fogg Art Museum, Harvard University, Purchase of the Louise E. Bettens Fund (1925.5.3).

Though trained early in life to be an artist, success and recognition came slowly to Demuth. In 1905 he studied with William Merritt Chase and Thomas Anshutz at the Pennsylvania Academy of Fine Arts, where he returned in 1908 after a trip to Europe. In 1912 he again traveled and studied in Europe, attending, among other schools, the Academie Julien. When the Fogg Museum acquired Charles Demuth's *Lily* in 1925, it became one of the first major museums in this country to endorse his art.

Demuth, like so many other American artists, chose to execute the bulk of his works in watercolor rather than oils. He usually reserved the more formal medium for his noteworthy and occasional industrial and imaginary scenes. Beside the continuing development of his major suites of mechanical images, Demuth's lyrical side emerged in his floral studies. Far from light diversions to his central concerns, these floral studies form a parallel and continuous accompaniment to the whole of his career.

Demuth's *Fruit and Sunflowers,* like other of his works, owes an acknowledged debt to European painting of the early decades of the century. This watercolor demonstrates his discriminating and subtle employment of Cubist invention, in this work not so much to dissolve apparent form but to give a certain ordered and systemic conviction to the bulk of the masses.

Pervading Demuth's watercolors of fruit, there seems to be an ever-present sense of strangeness. His fruits and flowers undergo a vaguely malevolent estrangement from their passive role as observed objects, and a suppressed air of perniciousness lingers even in bright daylight.

HZR

George Bellows 1882–1925

137 *Ringside Seats,* 1924

Lithographic crayon, litho ink, black india ink, white chalk; the design area is treated according to some unknown procedure and perhaps the drawing is executed over a printed lithograph; 22⅝ x 25⅞ inches

Signed lower left of center: Geo Bellows

Inscribed in pencil lower front, center: Ringside Seats — Drawn in 1924

Inscribed in pencil on verso: Pub. May 3/24 Chins of the Fathers by Jonathan Brooks ill by Geo Bellows.

Provenance: Sold by the artist's widow to Frederick Keppel & Co., New York, December 1938; Grenville L. Winthrop; Fogg Art Museum, Harvard University, Bequest of Grenville L. Winthrop (1943.567).

Bibliography: B. H. Hayes, Jr., *American Drawings,* New York, 1965, pl. 67.

138 *Sweeny, The Idol of the Fans, Had Hit a Home Run*

Lithographic crayon on white paper, 13 x 17½ inches

Signed lower center: Geo Bellows

Initialed lower left: G B

Provenance: Grenville L. Winthrop; Fogg Art Museum, Harvard University, Bequest of Grenville L. Winthrop (1943.568).

George Bellows, born in Columbus, Ohio, began his studies with Robert Henri in New York in 1904. By 1910 Bellows had settled into the house on East 19th Street which was to be his home until his death on 8 January 1925.

In 1916 he began to make lithographs, a medium particularly suited to his powerful line, and from 1921 he and his printer, Bolton Brown, experimented successfully with an increasingly wide range of lithographic tones.

Although under the spell of Jay Hambidge's complex theories of "Dynamic Symmetry," Bellows' work rarely lacked energy, which was sometimes evident in the depicted events and on other occasions surfaced as a democratic-populism reminiscent of Henri's (see No. 128). In the painting, which was completed in the same year as the drawing *Ringside Seats,* both of these kinds of energy are felt in the crowd, although the struggle of the contest is absent in the relaxed boxers themselves.

The complex technique of this drawing, layering one substance over another on treated paper, submerges the scene in a kind of icy brittleness, despite the noise and action of the crowd. The whole seems to shiver with a silvery, febrile evanescence.

In *Sweeny, The Idol of the Fans* ... the crowd is also the main active participant, but here after the fact of the accomplishment. All the light in the work falls on Sweeny savoring the best day of his life, appreciatively rubbing, and displaying, the muscles that swatted one over the fence. If one feels the artist's witty empathy for Sweeny, Bellow's experience also informed the drawing. While a student at Ohio State University, he acquired an outstanding reputation as a baseball player, and for a while he seriously considered a career as a professional player.

Bellows' line here often has the force of a bludgeon while at other times it is smudged and sooty, always in the service of the characters and never on display itself. The whole of this drawing recalls the flavor of another socially conscious artist, Daumier of *Les Gens de Justice*.

HZR

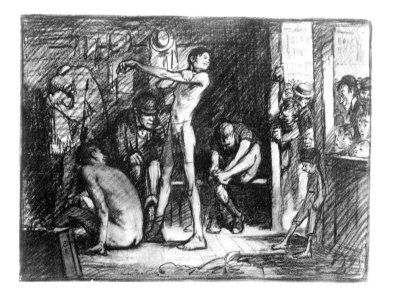

John Marin 1870–1953

139 *Mt. Chocorua,* 1926

Watercolor and charcoal on white paper, 17¼ x 22 inches

Signed and dated lower left: Marin 26

Provenance: Fogg Art Museum, Harvard University, Purchase of the Louise E. Bettens Fund (1928.4).

Bibliography: E. M. Benson, *John Marin: the Man and His Work,* Washington, D.C., 1935, pl. 33.

140 *White Mountain Country* (also called *The Presidential Range*), 1927

Watercolor and charcoal on white paper, 19⅙ x 24 inches (sight)

Signed and dated lower left: Marin 27

Provenance: Steiglitz Gallery, New York; Fogg Art Museum, Harvard University, Purchase of Friends of the Fogg Museum (1929.229).

Bibliography: H. Wish, *Society and Thought in Modern America,* New York, 2 vols. 1950–52.

It is difficult to come to grips with what the career and person of John Marin stood for in the period preceding and even during the ascendancy of American artists to a position of international leadership. Since Marin's death, his work has been undergoing a steady and methodical reevaluation, lifting the shroud which veiled his work in relative obscurity during the last years of his life. It is remarkable enough to think that in 1948 "Marin was voted America's greatest artist in a poll of museum directors and art critics" (C. Grey, ed., *John Marin by John Marin,* New York, 1970, 10).

Mt. Chocorua, like the bulk of his work, and like so much of that art that is peculiarly American, is a watercolor. Marin's forms are based simultaneously on his early training as an architect and on Cézanne's example of modeling. The artist's technical education is perhaps responsible for his concern with the massing of the form as well as his interest in the surrounding light and its effects as it envelops the mountain.

In 1914 Marin began roving the White Mountains of New Hampshire and for the first time passed the summer on the Maine coast. These two locales came to be rendered again and again in his flashing watercolors. Throughout these works, as in *White Mountain Country,* we see him attempting to enfold his subjects in a gem-like, glittering wrapper of air.

HZR

Gaston Lachaise 1882–1935

141 *"Acrobat" Upside-Down Figure,* 1927

Bronze, 10⅝ x 6⅝ x 3½ inches

Inscribed on base: G. Lachaise 1927

Provenance: Fogg Art Museum, Harvard University, Bequest of Marian H. Phinney (1962.78).

Bibliography: D. B. Goodall, *Gaston Lachaise, Sculptor,* unpublished Ph.D. dissertation, Harvard University, 1969, I, 492–494, II, 477.

142 *Floating Woman,* proof cast, ca. 1924–1927

Bronze, 12 x 17½ inches

Provenance: Fogg Art Museum, Harvard University, Anonymous Gift (1950.113).

Bibliography: H. Kramer, *Gaston Lachaise,* New York, 1967, pl. 33 (another cast is illustrated); D. B. Goodall, *Gaston Lachaise, Sculptor,* unpublished Ph.D. dissertation, Harvard University, 1969, I, 476–482, II, 422.

During a period when no American artist could think himself worthy of that title without having gone off to Europe for a while, Lachaise came from Paris to America to be an artist. He participated in the beginnings of a new art in this country and exhibited in the Armory Show of 1913. In his own words: "I can say that the New World is the most favorable place to develop a creative artist" (G. Lachaise, "A Comment on My Sculpture," *Creative Art,* 3, August 1928, xxiii).

The *"Acrobat"* of 1927 is one of Lachaise's numerous variations on the motif of the female form. This particular pose was slightly modified in 1929 in a larger, 20-inch version; in 1934, the theme reappeared in a more abstracted, machine-like work of 19¾ inches.

Of about the same period as the *"Acrobat"* is the *Floating Woman,* a proof cast of a small version of the large (51¾ x 96 inches) bronze *Floating Woman* (Museum of Modern Art, New York). This smaller piece has, however, generally more refined details and is more expressive and lyrical than the larger work. Lachaise's more complete control of this little work gives it the same masterful feel as Rodin's smaller pieces. Moreover, it appears that Lachaise actually wanted the woman to "float," suspended by a wire from above or a pipe from behind, to show the perfect balance and symmetry of the piece.

HZR

Charles Sheeler 1883–1965

143 *Upper Deck,* 1929

Oil on canvas, 29⅛ x 22⅛ inches

Signed and dated lower right: Sheeler '29

Provenance: The Downtown Gallery, New York; Fogg Art Museum, Harvard University, Purchase of the Louise E. Bettens Fund (1933.97).

Bibliography: J. Baur, *Revolution and Tradition in American Art,* Cambridge, Mass., 1951, pl. 74; M. Brown, *From the Armory Show to the Depression,* Princeton, New Jersey, 1952, 119; O. W. Larkin, *Art and Life in America,* New York, 1960; B. Rose, *American Painting: The Twentieth Century,* New York, 1969.

144 *Feline Felicity,* 1934

Conté crayon on white paper with a "RIVES" watermark, 22 x 18 inches

Signed and dated lower right: Sheeler 1934

Provenance: The Downtown Gallery, New York; Fogg Art Museum, Harvard University, Purchase of the Louise E. Bettens Fund (1934.182).

Bibliography: L. Dochterman, *The Quest of Charles Sheeler,* Iowa City, 1963, 25, repro. 14; D. Mendelowitz, *Drawing,* New York, 1967, pls. 1–3; M. Friedman, B. Hayes, and C. Millard, *Charles Sheeler,* Washington, D.C., 1968; E. Fish, *The Cat in Art,* Minneapolis, 1969.

In 1929 Charles Sheeler made his fourth trip to Europe and, principally as the result of seeing the early Italian masters, came away with the feeling that painting must have the internal logic of architecture or of a blueprint. Turning from photography, which had occupied him for the preceding years, he planned for a work of meticulous organization, glowing natural light, and a smooth crisp surface. The painting was to be crucial for Sheeler and a turning point for American art.

Upper Deck was that painting, and when it was completed Sheeler said of it: "This is what I have been getting ready for. I had come to feel that a picture could have incorporated in it the structural design implied in abstraction and be presented in a wholly realist manner" (C. Rourke, *Charles Sheeler, Artist in the American Tradition,* New York, 1938, 142).

As a rejoinder to criticism that he could only paint the mechanical and unfeeling contrivances of technology, Sheeler made the highly finished drawing *Feline Felicity*, but where precision had lent authority to his monumental industrial scenes, the same degree of finish, doubtless derived from a photograph, rendered a living subject unnaturally rigidified. Despite the conviction with which the sun pours in over the Shaker chair and its wicker seat on which a brindled cat snoozes, the whole seems almost too fastidious to contain life. The piece is, nevertheless, a forceful and irrefutable display of Sheeler's abundant talents as a draughtsman.

HZR

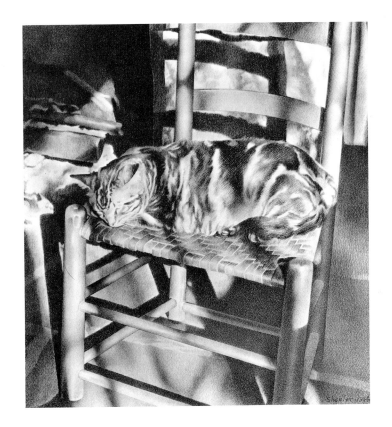

Hyman Bloom   1913–

145   *Wrestlers,* ca. 1930

Black crayon on brown paper, 10⅛ x 14⅙ inches

Provenance: The artist to Dr. Denman W. Ross; Fogg Art Museum, Harvard University, Bequest of Dr. Denman W. Ross (1936.94).

Hyman Bloom, born near Riga, Latvia, came to live in Boston at the age of seven; since then he has rarely left the city. In 1929 he, like Jack Levine, came to the attention of Denman Ross of Harvard University. Both boys were given studios and further instruction by Ross himself.

The *Wrestlers,* which is actually one side of a large sheet of studies, doubtless comes from this early period of Ross's tutelage. The verso is covered with numerous sketches including a head, an ear, a nude back, all quick but highly competent. In this early phase of Bloom's artistic investigation, his skill, primarily as a draughtsman, remarkable as it was to become, is already amply evident.

HZR

Edward Hopper 1882–1967

146 *Highland Light,* 1930

Watercolor, 15⅝ x 24½ inches

Signed lower right: Edward Hopper–Cape Cod

Provenance: Frank K. M. Rehn Gallery; Fogg Art Museum, Harvard University, Purchase of the Louise E. Bettens Fund (1930.462).

Bibliography: L. Goodrich, *Edward Hopper,* New York, 1971, 212.

Hopper studied at the New York School of Art under Robert Henri (see No. 128) and Kenneth H. Miller. He made the last of his three trips to Europe in 1910. Although he was represented in the Armory Show of 1913, it was not until the 1920's that he achieved recognition with a show of watercolors in 1924 and representation in a show of living American artists at the Museum of Modern Art in 1929.

Highland Light belongs to a theme which Hopper began painting on summer trips to Cape Elizabeth and Portland Head in Maine during the mid-1920's. This lighthouse from North Truro is near the house that he bought on Cape Cod at South Truro in 1930. This work displays Hopper's ability to capture the character of a place and to use patterns of light and shade as major compositional elements in a simplifying approach to form. His watercolors are quite naturalistic, and they generally reveal the natural transparency of the medium. The foreground in this work shows that he did not always rise above the technical difficulties of the medium, as he seemed to be aware when he said: "I have tried to present my sensations in what is the most congenial and impressive form for me. The technical obstacles of painting perhaps dictate this form" (Goodrich, *Edward Hopper,* 161).

KCB

147 *Locomotives Watering,* 1932

Pencil on white paper, 9⅜ x 12½ inches

Provenance: Fogg Art Museum, Harvard University, Gift of Mrs. Reginald Marsh (1962.256).

Reginald Marsh was born in Paris, the son of artist parents; in 1900 he came home, first to New Jersey and then to New York. Marsh trained mainly at Yale and, in the period 1920–1924, at the Art Students League in New York, where his most notable teachers were George Luks and John Sloan.

Although conventionally classified a "social-realist," Marsh would have preferred to have himself described as a man whose heart was with the Italian sixteenth century. A draughtsman, he sought out in the urban and industrial landscape the flow of figurative compositions reminiscent of the old masters.

The drawing *Locomotives Watering* is apparently a study for a 1932 painting with the same title. In 1934 an etching in seven states and an edition of eighteen, called *Erie R. R. Locos Watering,* was made from this same pencil study. The two later renditions of the composition, painted and etched, are remarkably similar to the initial pencil drawing, an indication of the regard Marsh himself held for the soundness of this arrangement.

HZR

Charles E. Burchfield 1893–1967

148 *Old Farm House (September Sunlight)*, 1932

Watercolor on white paper, 14⅞ x 21 inches

Signed and dated lower left with monogram: ℣Ꮧ 1932

Provenance: Frank K. M. Rehn Gallery, New York; Fogg Art Museum, Harvard University, Purchase of the Louise E. Bettens Fund (1938.28).

Bibliography: J. S. Trovato, *Charles Burchfield Catalogue of Paintings in Public and Private Collections* [exhibition catalogue], Munson-Williams-Proctor Institute, Utica, N.Y., 1970, no. 84.

149 *March Sunlight*, 1926–1934

Watercolor on white paper, 24⅜ x 33¼ inches

Signed lower left with monogram: ℣Ꮧ

Provenance: Frank K. M. Rehn Gallery, New York; Fogg Art Museum, Harvard University, Purchase of the Louise E. Bettens Fund (1934.63).

Bibliography: J. S. Trovato, *Charles Burchfield Catalogue of Paintings in Public and Private Collections* [exhibition catalogue], Munson-Williams-Proctor Institute, Utica, N.Y., 1970, no. 825.

Charles Burchfield was born in Ashtabula Harbor, Ohio. Awarded a scholarship to study in New York, he left school after only one day of classes returning, from a short trying stay in the city, to his family.

It would be just as accurate to say that he returned to an interrupted enthrallment with nature, a love from which he strayed again only fleeting in the 1940's to paint the landscape of industry.

The *Old Farm House (September Sunlight)* was executed from a pencil drawing of New Albany, Ohio, one of Burchfield's childhood homes. The old building sinks into the land from which it has risen and returns to the earth its parcel of memories. Such a rhapsodic response to this work does not seem to be out of keeping with Burchfield's own intentions. Though accurate, in fact precise, renditions of locations are the mainstay of much of Burchfield's work, his pieces are never mere reportage.

Burchfield faced the tangible world and imbued nature with a wonder that makes the actually perceived teem with fantastic possibilities. These conceptions were not easily won or simply ornaments on a scaffold of apparent perception; rather, the internal life of things, as in *March Sunlight*, had to be deeply felt and the rendition of that force was not a glib affair.

"Canyon" in the Cattaraugus Creek (the point at the center marks the confluence of the East and West branches) about a mile east of Gowanda, New York. The effect sought here is of the late afternoon sunlight in the early Spring, when young trees seem to bristle with up-shooting growth. I made this sketch in 1926, never felt satisfied with it, and seven years later went back to the same spot, on the same kind of day, and reworked it, using what I had as a sort of "under-painting". To me the little islands in the center were like a dream world, or fairy land come to life (Trovato, *Burchfield*, 825).

An expectant energy hangs over this crisp scene, and the audience can be very sure that what is pictured is not a view of an arrangement of the landscape, but the entry into a dream of nature.

HZR

Rico Lebrun   1900–1964

150   *Crouching Girl,* 1932

Conté crayon on red-brown paper, squared for transfer in graphite, 29½ x 21½ inches

Signed middle right: Lebrun / Roma 1932

Provenance: Fogg Art Museum, Harvard University, Gift of Rico Lebrun, Esq. (1933.147).

Rico Lebrun came to America in 1924, the foreman of a stained-glass factory in Springfield, Illinois. After one year at the factory, he moved to New York to begin a career first as a very popular commercial artist, and later as a foremost portrayer of the human figure. In 1933 he and Louis Rubenstein, companions in Rome, produced a mural for the top floor of the Fogg Museum. This fresco, completed just after Lebrun's return from Europe and now partially covered over, is suggested by the scale of the *Crouching Girl* drawing, done shortly before his return to America.

Although he investigated and employed the human figure primarily as an element for the scope of epic compositions, this early drawing shows the delicacy of the Latin tradition of draughting, just as the great, writhing scenes of carnage were to mine another aspect of that heritage.

Even his famous studies for the Crucifixion, the fitful musings on Dacchau, or the illustrations for Dante's *Inferno* do not completely epitomize a rounded view of Rico Lebrun's talents. He was an inspired teacher, who instructed at New York's Art Students League beginning in 1936, and whose varied assignments included work on Walt Disney's *Bambi.*

HZR

Anna Hyatt Huntington   1876–

151   *Speedy,* 1935

Bronze, 16¼ x 20½ inches

Signed on base: Anna Hyatt Huntington

Provenance: Archer M. Huntington; Fogg Art Museum, Harvard University, Gift of Archer M. Huntington (1943.1845).

Bibliography: E. M. Mellon, *Anna Hyatt Huntington,* New York, 1947, 31 (another cast); E. Scaub-Kock, *L'Oeuvre d'Anna Huntington,* Paris, 1949, 136.

Anna Hyatt Huntington was born in Cambridge, Massachusetts, the daughter of Alpheus Hyatt, a noted palaeontologist at Harvard. Notably, she studied with Gutzon Borglum (see No. 127) and for a time at the Art Students League of New York.

Speedy, the greyhound, is very much a part of the mainstream of her development as a sculptor. Her first show, in 1898, was an exhibit of animal studies. Later, Anna Hyatt Huntington became celebrated for her monumental and conservatively romantic pieces which adorn so many of the great plazas of this country.

HZR

David Smith 1906–1965

152 *The Artist Photographing a Female Torso,*
1937

Grey tempera and india ink on white paper,
7 x 10 inches

Dated lower right: 1937

Provenance: Fogg Art Museum, Harvard University, Gift of David Smith (1966.33).

This drawing of 1937 dates from about the same time that David Smith began to produce his "medals for dishonor," a series of devastating appraisals of the causes and effects of war. We see him here in a more relaxed, though hardly less witty mood. This clever, warm drawing gives a lively impression of the artist's cluttered studio in the year of his first sale, a sculpture which brought him $8.

HZR

Pavel Tchelitchew 1898–1957

153 *Frederick Ashton,* 1938

Silver point on white prepared paper, 20 x 12½ inches

Signed and dated lower right: P. Tchelitchew London 1938

Provenance: Durlacher Brothers Gallery, Boston; Fogg Art Museum, Harvard University, Gift of Meta and Paul J. Sachs (1959.165).

Bibliography: L. Kirstein, *Pavel Tchelitchew,* New York, 1947, pl. 33; D. Mendelowitz, *Drawing,* New York, 1967, pls. 16-17.

Pavel Tchelitchew, born in Moscow, came to the United States in 1934 after a cosmopolitan education and success in Europe. He became a naturalized citizen in 1952 and died in Rome in 1957 shortly before he was to return to America. Without doubt, his greatest work begins with the period in which he first took up residence in this country.

This elegant drawing of Sir Frederick William Mallandine Ashton dates from a time before the sitter became widely celebrated. Tchelitchew knew Ashton before he became Director of the Royal Ballet, in fact knew him from 1929, when Ashton was a member of the company of Madame Ida Rubenstein. Tchelitchew was in London at the time of this drawing (May 1938), preparing costumes and scenery for the Ballet Russe de Monte Carlo and the Leonide Massine-Paul Hindemith ballet *Nobilissima Visione,* which opened July 21, 1938, at Drury Lane.

HZR

Milton Avery   1893–1965

154   *Still Life with Woman,* 1946

Oil on canvas, 39½ x 29½ inches

Provenance: Fogg Art Museum, Harvard University, Gift of Dr. Harold Gershinowitz (1966.85).

Milton Avery was self-taught, with the exception of one life-drawing class he attended in Hartford for a short while in 1911. His life seems to have been a bright journey beyond the turmoil of the great developments in art during his lifetime: his works do not display any sense of apparent internal struggle; his images do not seem to solicit participation from dogma. In fact his calm world was devoid of all excesses, the dross of intellectual fad, the unessential, or the pure embellishment. He once remarked, "Why talk when you can paint?" (A. D. Breeskin, *Milton Avery* [exhibition catalogue], New York Graphic Society, Greenwich, Conn., 1970, 1.

Avery's world, so drenched in loveliness, would seem to have little force or appeal for the generation of vigorous explorers who were to follow him, and yet a great testimony to his paintings' importance was established by the continuing reverence paid him by Adolph Gottlieb and Mark Rothko. In many ways Avery prefigured this later era with his accent on surface pattern, shape, and an intense pallet, though all the while his images energetically defend their identity.

HZR

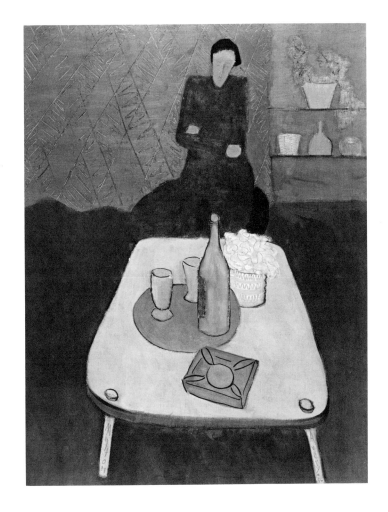

William Baziotes 1912–1963

155 *Bird of Paradise,* 1947

Oil on canvas, 37½ x 29½ inches (sight)

Signed lower right: Baziotes

Provenance: Fogg Art Museum, Harvard University, Purchase of the Louise E. Bettens Fund (1949.51).

William Baziotes did not, like so many of his generation, turn away from a figurative art to one of purely formal invention and arrangement. Instead, mining his own unconscious for images, he tried to root his looming apprehensions in forms culled from the scope of global culture. Images like *Bird of Paradise* often seem to dwell in a submarine world of limited vistas, nebulous shapes, and impenetrable atmosphere. It is from this condition that his figures emerge as from the throes of delirium rather than from the unflinching, meticulous, analysis of Dali or Tanguy.

Though his titles often seem specific enough, their relationship to the works need not be thought of as a binding limit. Only after the fact of the work's emotional impact does a distinct identity of actual subject matter become an issue for the viewer. It appears to have been thus for Baziotes also: "Often I recognize my subject at completion of the picture and again I may wait a long time before I know what it is about" (W. Baziotes, personal statement, 1945, David Porter Gallery). Most often when an image did clarify itself, the label that was applied was that of a known mythic being, and usually one fixed in the constellation of some epic.

HZR

Robert Motherwell 1915–

156 *The Elegy,* 1948

Painting, collage, glazed, 29½ x 24 inches (sight)

Signed lower right: Motherwell '48

Provenance: Samuel M. Kootz Gallery, New York; Fogg Art Museum, Harvard University, Purchase of the Louise E. Bettens Fund (1949.49).

Bibliography: Smith College, *Robert Motherwell* [exhibition catalogue], Northampton, Mass., 1963, pl. 4; F. O'Hara, *Robert Motherwell* [exhibition catalogue], Museum of Modern Art, New York, 1965, 15.

After undergraduate study at a few schools, Robert Motherwell graduated in 1936 from Stanford, where he majored in philosophy. The next year saw him enrolled in Harvard's Graduate School of Arts and Sciences to pursue his studies in the Department of Philosophy. After more study at the University of Grenoble, at Oxford, and at Columbia University, he began his career as a painter and teacher, notably in association with Black Mountain College in 1945 and 1951.

To date, Motherwell's most important series of paintings have been his *Elegies,* whose principal black and brooding motif was invented while experimenting in 1948 with page ornament for a book of poems by Harold Rosenberg. Motherwell has said of this series: "I take an elegy to be a funeral lamentation or funeral song for something one cared about ... that should not be forgot. They are as eloquent as I could make them. But the pictures are also general metaphors of the contrast between life and death, and their interrelation" (Smith College, *Robert Motherwell,* pl. 16).

The Elegy, a comparatively diminutive collage, antedates and is ancestral to the massive *Elegies to the Spanish Republic.* This earlier blue, more gentle, and colorful work is a pristine model compared with the later huge and brutal paintings of the same name.

HZR

Jackson Pollock 1912–1956

157 *Number 2, 1950*

Oil, lacquer, duco, silver paint, pebbles, etc., on canvas, 113 x 36 inches

Signed upper right: Jackson Pollock

Inscribed on stretcher in grease crayon, a not uncommon feature of Pollock's "drip paintings": Jackson Pollock Number 2, 1950

Provenance: Mrs. Jackson Pollock; Mr. and Mrs. Reginald R. Isaacs; Fogg Art Museum, Harvard University, Gift of Mr. and Mrs. Reginald R. Isaacs and Family and Purchase of the Contemporary Art Fund (1965.554).

In *Number 2, 1950,* color is more precisely contrived than simply exuberant or articulate of mood, and this precision of piquant consonances lends to the vertical architecture a severe but distinct personality. Viewed as a possible horizontal painting, the very architecture which so clearly excites under the tension of the vertical format, with its allusive implications of the stress of erecting a mass in air, devolves into a massive repose. The decision for the vertical is amply justified.

When we talk about quality in the work of Pollock, we seem finally to be talking about the personality of each work, of how distinct and palpable that identity has become in terms of the means of generation. In evaluations of works by this American master, questions arise with especial force, as with no previous painter; for example: whether rhythm in draughting has aided the color; how sequences of color were laid down and whether these sequences are overlaid by obscuring pattern the contribution and propriety of scale; the selection of edge; the choice of vertical or horizontal format.

Number 2, 1950 satisfactorily epitomizes the last year of Pollock's total commitment to drip technique. Later he was to work largely in black and white and then strike out in a renewed exploration of figuration. Thus this painting captures a crucial moment at the virtual apex of what can only be termed a classic style, a style whose progress was cut short by the artist's untimely demise.

HZR

Alexander Calder 1898–

158 *Little Blue under Red,* ca. 1950

Iron-like composition, painted black, red, blue, and white, 58 x 82 inches

Provenance: The artist; Fogg Art Museum, Harvard University, Purchase of the Louise E. Bettens Fund (1955.99).

Bibliography: B. Rose, *American Art Since 1900,* New York, 1968, 247-248, repro. 9-10.

Alexander Calder, the son and grandson of sculptors, is easily one of the greatest figures of twentieth-century sculpture and one of but a handful of Americans to have achieved worldwide fame. His mobiles have added the elements of movement to sculpture without making this apparent synthesis visible as such, or gesturing toward doctrine.

Little Blue under Red fulfills the role of grounded stationary sculpture in the articulation of the base (the stabile) while the kinetic element is contributed by a freely moving upper portion (the mobile). The artist, in a letter, has dated the work as being from around 1950.

HZR

Franz Kline 1910–1962

159 *Composition,* 1952

Oil on canvas, 54 x 33¾ inches

Inscribed on back: Franz Kline Egan Gallery

Provenance: Egan Gallery, New York; G. David Thompson; Fogg Art Museum, Harvard University, Gift of G. David Thompson in memory of his son, G. David Thompson, Jr., Class of 1958 (1959.17).

Whatever reverential language is rightly used to describe Franz Kline's late work, it should be remembered that for most of his professional life he labored in equally deserved obscurity as a mildly successful Realist. The break came as he formulated his huge black and white autographic style.

This was not basically a bleak architectural exercise in two dimensions; but completely utilizing the full range of greys and a variety of textures, Kline transformed what could have been the neutral limits of an art of grisaille into a remarkable coloristic vocabulary. Rather than a feeling of design and pattern, which would have resulted from the pure alternation of his two hues, a sense of fullness and great, even heroic, presence derived from gradations in tone, and the resultant feeling of depth inheres in his painting.

Passages in the *Composition* can be seen as rendered black on white, or areas of white successively appear as spaces in the black. In either case the rapid shift in resolution prevents the work from appearing as mere pattern. Kline's paintings were not quickly shaped; often months went into the working and reworking of a gesture to secure a succinct and precisely expressive image.

HZR

Ben Shahn 1898–1969

160 *Sacco and Vanzetti,* 1952

Ink on white paper, 5¾ x 8⅜ inches (sight)

Signed lower right: Ben Shahn

Provenance: The Downtown Gallery, New York; Paul J. Sachs; Fogg Art Museum, Harvard University, Gift of Meta and Paul J. Sachs (1956.184).

Bibliography: J. T. Soby, *Ben Shahn: His Graphic Art,* New York, 1967, 63.

Bartolomeo Vanzetti and Nicola Sacco were executed on 23 August 1927, and an inconsolable Ben Shahn walked the streets of Brooklyn, alone and crying that day. The case and its two victims continued to haunt the artist throughout his career. In 1931 Shahn wrote: "I had seen all the right pictures and read all the right books—Vollard, Meier-Graefe, Hulme—but still it didn't add up to anything. Here I am, I said to myself, thirty-two years old, the son of a carpenter. I like stories and people. The French School is not for me. If I am to be a painter I must show how the world looks through my eyes, not theirs . . . . Then I got to thinking about the Sacco-Vanzetti case again" (S. Rodman, *Ben Shahn: Portrait as an American,* New York, 1951, 117).

His thinking that year led him to produce twenty-three gouaches, all based on the trial; one of these, a double portrait of the anarchists in chains, closely resembles this drawing of 1952. The drawing is undoubtedly the basis for a serigraph, made in 1958, that agrees with the drawing in all but the smallest particulars. Appended beneath both the drawing and the later serigraph is a colophon transcribed by Philip Strong as spoken by Vanzetti shortly before his death.

Ben Shahn put his art in the service of a personal moral position, in marked contrast to the formal, silent investigations of much American art before the late twenties. Moreover his art remained at a consistently high level of quality throughout his life, never descending to mere *agitprop.*

HZR

"If it had not been for these thing, I might have live out my life talking at street corners to scorning men. I might have die, unmarked, unknown, a failure. Now we are not a failure. This is our career and our triumph. Never in our full life could we hope to do such work for tolerance, for justice, for man's understanding of man as now we do by accident. Our words—our lives—our pains nothing! The taking of our lives—lives of a good shoemaker and a poor fish peddler—all! That last moment belongs to us— that agony is our triumph." ▄ Bartolomeo Vanzetti

Jack Levine 1915–

161 *King Asa,* 1953

Oil on canvas board, 10 x 8 inches

Signed lower left: J. Levine

Provenance: Paul J. Sachs; Fogg Art Museum, Harvard University, Gift of Meta and Paul J. Sachs (1963.446).

Bibliography: F. Getlein, *Jack Levine,* New York, 1959, no. 69.

Born in Boston, Jack Levine received his first artistic training at a community center in Roxbury; subsequent drawing instruction at the Museum of Fine Arts brought him and Hyman Bloom (see No. 145) to the attention of Denman W. Ross of Harvard. In 1929 Professor Ross gave both boys studios and weekly allowances of $12, but he also opened to them the treasures of the past.

In the portrait of *King Asa* Levine plays upon one of the great heritages in the repertoire of Western art, the intimate, miniature portrait. Levine's painting of Asa, a figure in Kings II and Chronicles II, is one of a series of imaginary portraits of Old Testament kings, prophets, and teachers which the artist made as a memorial to his father.

In this painting, the old, righteous king, who had pulled down the idols in the land and reformed the kingdom, takes the sun and naps with a clear conscience. This imaginary portrait is clearly the corresponding positive statement, in strongly implied contrast, to the satire of capitalist decadence and political corruption that forms the bulk of Levine's work.
HZR

Morris Louis 1912–1962

162 *Blue Veil,* 1958-1959

Acrylic resin paint on canvas, 100½ x 14. inches

Provenance: Mrs. Abner Brenner (the artist's widow). André Emmerich Gallery, New York; Mrs. Culver Orswell; Fogg Art Museum, Harvard University, Gift of Mrs. Culver Orswell in association with the Museum's Fund for Special Uses (1965.28).

Bibliography: Guggenheim Museum, *Morris Louis Memorial Exhibition,* New York, 1963, no. 9; M. Fried, "Blue Veil by Morris Louis," *Fogg Art Museum Acquisitions, 1965,* Cambridge, Mass., 1966, 177-181; M. Fried, *Morris Louis,* New York, 1971, no. 33.

Born Morris Bernstein in Baltimore, Maryland, the artist attended, but did not graduate from, the Baltimore City College and the Maryland Institute of Fine and Applied Arts. After holding several odd jobs in his hometown, he moved to New York in 1936 and sometime thereafter took the surname Louis. Having shown a painting in the 1939 World's Fair, Morris Louis returned to Baltimore and subsequently married. His career might have continued to read like that of so many other artists who came to New York in the thirties and were caught up in the tempo of that city's artistic life, only to return home to local notoriety and mild success, had not his work taken an abrupt turn.

In 1954 Louis developed the technique of staining large areas of raw cotton duck with brilliant streams of overlapping color. This simple description gives no hint of the formal problems—mainly the legacy of Pollock, but also issues raised by Helen Frankenthaler and Franz Kline—that the application of this technique rendered possible to resolve. Nor does it hint at the lyric beauty of these glowing works.

Blue Veil is unquestionably one of the masterpieces of Louis' art, combining as it does a fabulous visual lusciousness and a stringent adherence to the dictates of method. Like so much of the work that was to follow in the tradition established by Louis' method, the wall-size scale, rather than appearing ponderous, is delicate and ethereal because of the transparency of the staining technique.

HZR

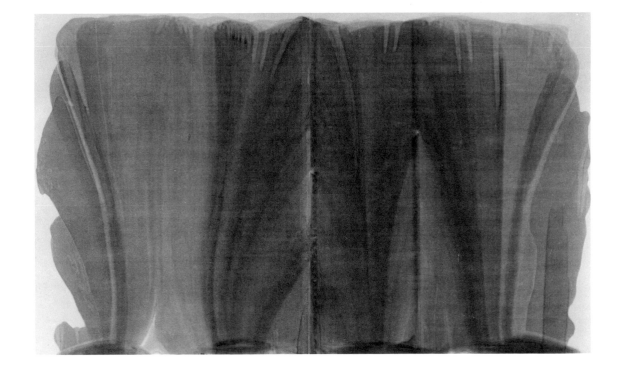

Morris Louis

163 *Color Barrier,* 1961

Acrylic resin (Magna medium) on canvas, 91⅜ x 60 inches

Provenance: André Emmerich Gallery, New York; Fogg Art Museum, Harvard University, Purchase of the Louise E. Bettens Fund (1963.105).

Bibliography: M. Fried, *Morris Louis,* New York, 1971, no. 158.

Morris Louis' *Color Barrier* is an example of the artist's use of intense and pure color, applied to the canvas without blending, to set up a configuration yielding a system of tonal harmonies. The colors themselves, applied without any hint of the external means by which they were administered, carry the weight of expression assisted by the thrust of the colors' vertical axis. This work and its format are typical of the paintings Louis executed in 1961 and 1962, brilliant in their own regard and an interesting counterpoint in their smaller scale to the huge "unfurleds."

HZR

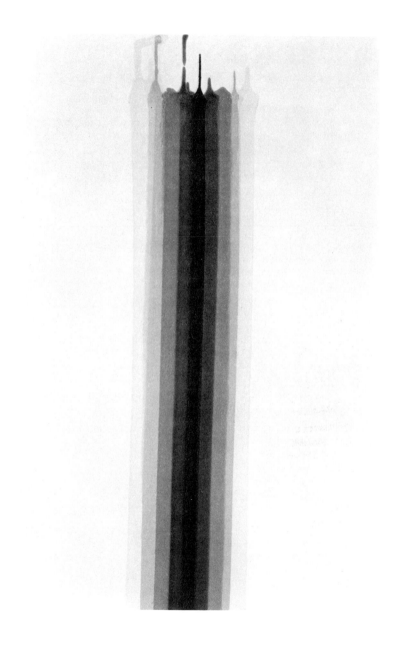

Kenneth Noland 1924–

164 *Karma,* 1964

Acrylic resin paint on canvas, 102 x 144 inches

Provenance: Fogg Art Museum, Harvard University, Gift of Kenneth Noland (1965.22).

Bibliography: M. Fried, *Three American Painters* [exhibition catalogue], Fogg Art Museum, Cambridge, Mass., 1965, 2.

In the work of Pollock, Kline, and then Morris Louis, shape was generated with the application of color. Kenneth Noland's "hard edge" disposition of paint released shape from its obligation to reflect and obviate the processes of the act of painting. Shape, as such, could act as an independent component, correlated to, but not intrinsic with, the application and hence the development of the color tonality. Freed to experiment with the disposition of shape, Noland successively employed "Targets," "Lozenges"; in 1962 he started to paint his "Chevrons" series.

Karma is one of the latter. In it the shapes are generated by the two variables of the angle of the chevron and the location of the point of their origin, here asymmetrically disposed, with regard to the enframement of the whole rectangular surface. A sprawling, generous, open space, the painting is dated in 1964 in a letter by the artist.

HZR

165 *Secretary Desk,* 1755–1795

Mahogany (white pine), height 106¼ inches (lower case 45¼ inches), width 46 inches, depth 23¼ inches (open 34 inches)

Provenance: The President's House, 17 Quincy Street, Harvard University (donor unknown).

Not only is this secretary one of the finest pieces at Harvard, but it is one of the major examples of American furniture. The bombé, or kettle-base, form is the most baroque of American designs. Its use is believed to have been confined to the Boston area, and even there its occurrence is rare. Deriving its inspiration from the Continent, probably by way of England, it displays massive grandeur. Paw feet, usually confined to superb Massachusetts pieces, have shaped brackets whose form is repeated at the center. The feet support the swelling base which uses the better of the two known drawer arrangements. Here their outer edge follows the curve of the side rather than being squared off. The edge of the base is outlined with a carved molding, another rare refinement, and the desk interior is blocked and carved to two types of fans. The upper section has two doors with shaped and edge-molded matched grain panels flanked by pilaster strips supporting Corinthian capitals. Above a cornice molding, the scroll-arched pediment supports three corkscrew finials typical of Massachusetts. (The urn of the center finial is a later replacement.)

JTK

Boston or Salem

166 *Card Table,* 1755–1795

Mahogany (maple back rail and gate, tulip poplar inner back rail; one knee bracket a replacement, one missing), height 29 inches, width 29½ inches, depth 15¾ inches

Provenance: Joseph Willard (1738–1804); his son Joseph (1798–1865); his son Robert (1838–1892); his daughter Theodora (1870–1937); Harvard University, Bequest of Miss Theodora Willard, 1937 (226.1953).

Bibliography: Harvard University, *Furniture and Decorative Arts of the Period 1636–1836* [exhibition catalogue, Harvard Tercentenary Exhibition], Cambridge, Mass., 1936, no. 251.

According to family tradition, this table, like Nos. 169 and 171, belonged to Joseph Willard (1738–1804), President of Harvard (1781–1804).

Card tables with serpentine-shaped skirts were made from Boston to Charleston, South Carolina, and those with an echoing serpentine lower edge are usually associated with Newport, Rhode Island. However, the form of this table's claws and ball feet, with their retracted side claws, and the use of arrised knees suggests a Boston or Salem origin. Typical of much of the finest American work, it depends on elegance of line rather than elaborate decoration.

JTK

John Dane (?)   1749–1829

167   *Secretary Desk,* 1755–1774

Mahogany (white pine), height 87 inches (lower case 43¼ inches), width 43⅝ inches, depth 25 inches (open 38 inches)

Provenance: (according to tradition) Nathan Dane (1752–1835); his sister Molly Dane Ellingwood (1758–1839); her daughter Fanny Ellingwood Larcom (1780–1847); her daughter Fanny Larcom Hale (1807–1883); her son Edwin Hale Abbot (1834–1927); his son Edwin Hale Abbot, Jr. (1881–1966); Fogg Art Museum, Harvard University, Gift of Edwin H. Abbot, Jr. (1950.167).

Bibliography: Mary A. Parsons, *Ancestry of Nathan Dane Dodge and his wife Sarah (Shepherd) Dodge,* Salem, Mass., 1896, 11.

According to Parsons this secretary was made by Samuel Dane (1745–1777) of Beverly, Massachusetts for his brother Nathan (1752–1835), founder of the Dane Professorship of Law (Parsons, *Nathan Dane Dodge,* 11; confirmed by handwritten notes on endpaper by Francis E. Abbot, 1897). But, the top of the lower case is inscribed "John Dane," who was also a cabinetmaker, and the piece is probably by him. This block-front secretary, like the bombé secretary (No. 165) echoes the baroque of Europe. Typical of Eastern Massachusetts work are the use of a shell-carved drop below the base molding, the form of the desk interior, and the shape of its fans, round headed panels flanked by pilaster strips, a shell on the pediment and corkscrew finials. (The center finial is a replacement. The side finials should be supported on higher bases). Unusual for Massachusetts are the stylized quality of the pediment shell and the cut out leafage on the edge of the plinth supporting the central finial; these are more like rural Connecticut work.

JTK

168 *Side Chair,* 1755–1795

Mahogany (oak slip seat frame and rear seat rail), height 38 inches, width 23¼ inches, seat height 16½ inches

Provenance: Joseph Willard (1738-1804); his son Joseph (1798–1865); his son Robert (1838–1892); his daughter, Theodora (1870–1937); Harvard University, Bequest of Miss Theodora Willard, 1937 (218.1953).

Bibliography: Harvard University, *Furniture and Decorative Arts of the Period 1636–1836* [exhibition catalogue, Harvard Tercentenary Exhibition], Cambridge, Mass., 1936, no. 252, pl. 45.

This chair is part of a set of six which according to family tradition belonged to Joseph Willard (1738–1804), President of Harvard (1781-1804). Typical of Massachusetts Chippendale chairs is the use of cabriole legs with arrised knees, simple curved knee-brackets with C-scroll drops, a thin seat rail without shaping on its lower edge, rear legs that flare at their base, and a crest rail with blunt ears. The use of a splat pierced to a figure-eight with a diamond center, below stylized drapery above a tassel, is known in other style centers, but its enclosure within a shield-shaped outline and its almost brittle feel are confined to the Boston-Salem area, although all of these features appear in England.

Stop-fluted back posts are rare in America, but they are known on Boston and English chairs. Unusual for Eastern Massachusetts is the form of the feet with their webless, elongated claws on a tall ball. The standard Massachusetts foot is like that of No. 166, and sometimes it is like that of No. 167.

JTK

169 *Side Chair,* 1790–1810

Mahogany, mahogany veneer (ash), height 36½ inches, width 20½ inches, seat height 16½ inches

Provenance: Joseph Willard (1738–1804); his son Joseph (1798–1865); his son Robert (1838–1892); his daughter Theodora (1870–1937); Harvard University, Bequest of Miss Theodora Willard, 1937 (420.1942).

Bibliography: Harvard University, *Furniture and Decorative Arts of the Period 1636–1836* [exhibition catalogue, Harvard Tercentenary Exhibition], Cambridge, Mass., 1936, No. 254.

According to tradition, this chair is from a set of four which belonged to Joseph Willard (1738–1804), President of Harvard (1781–1804). After the American Revolution the new simplified designs that dominated English furniture quickly altered American furniture designs. Streamlined intellectual conceits produced posed elegance which overrode sound, sturdy construction. One of the few basic chair designs used square backs with several patterned "splats." Here Gothic arching with stylized leafage "supports" the inlaid and line-edged crest-rail panel. The corners of the back are carved to floral dies. The outer faces of the front legs, the fronts of the back posts above the seat, the "pillars" of the arcading and of the lower rail of the back are reeded. Related chairs, but with a light veneer in the crest-rail panel as well as uncarved corners and parallel rather than flaring back posts, have been assigned to Boston (Richard H. Randall, Jr., *American Furniture,* Boston 1965, no. 171; Charles Montgomery, *The Federal Period 1788–1825,* New York, 1966, no. 25).

JTK

170   *Side Chair,* 1810–1825

Mahogany, mahogany veneer on crest rail
(white pine), height 33 inches, width 18 inches,
seat height 15½ inches

Provenance: The President's House, 17 Quincy
Street, Harvard University (donor unknown).

These chairs use the Greek klismos form that,
unlike earlier American chairs, places the
movement or action of the chair at the sides.
The back curves into the seat, and it curves
into the sabre legs. The two sides are con-
nected by a concave carved and paneled crest
rail, paired scrolls holding a rosette, a reeded
front, and a back rail.

ITK

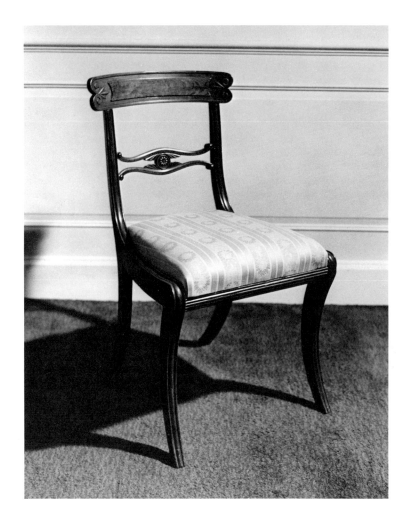

American

171 *Cabinet-Desk,* 1815–1835

Mahogany, maple; mahogany, maple veneers; ormolu (pine, tulip, poplar), height 62½ inches, width 46 inches, depth 22¼ inches (open 39½ inches)

Provenance: Fogg Art Museum, Harvard University, Gift of Murray Anthony Potter and Bessie Lincoln Potter (1957.22).

This desk is based on French Empire designs that became popular in the American style centers about 1815. They use a tightly closed volume with a thin surface decoration of elaborately matched veneers with ormolu accents, flanked at the front corners by pillars. The front panel opens to reveal an architectural fantasy with a mirrored back.

JTK

172 *Caudle Cup, "The Holyoke Cup,"* ca. 1690

Silver, height 5 inches, diameter base 4¹⁵⁄₁₆ inches, weight 23 ounces 13 dwt.

Marks: "IC" above a fleur-de-lys, in a heart-shaped punch on the back

Engraved in the nineteenth century with the Holyoke arms and inscribed on the front below lip: Duce Natura Sequor

Provenance: Rev. Edward Holyoke; his daughter Elizabeth Holyoke Kneeland; her son-in-law Professor Levi Hedge; Fred H. Hedge; Charlotte Hedge; Harvard University, Bequest of Miss Charlotte Hedge (878.1927).

Bibliography: H. F. Clark, *John Coney, Silversmith, 1655–1722,* Boston and New York, 1932, 29-30 pl. 9; Harvard University, *Furniture and Decorative Arts of the Period 1636–1836* [exhibition catalogue, Harvard Tercentenary Exhibition], Cambridge, Mass., 1936, no. 91, pl. 18; J. M. Phillips, *American Silver,* New York, 1949, 33; K. C. Buhler, "Harvard College Plate," *The Connoisseur Year Book,* 1955, 52, no. ii; G. Hood, *American Silver: A History of Style, 1650–1900,* London and New York, 1971, 29, pl. 7.

Attached to this gourd-shaped cup with an embossed band of floral sprays and cherubim are two scrolled handles with caryatid grips. The seamless body is raised by hammer-work from a disc of silver; the beaded handles are cast. The decorative ornament on the wide panel of the cup illustrates Coney's early use of repoussé-work, a method utilizing a snarling iron on the inside of the vessel, combined with hammer- and punch-work on the outside.

This caudle cup belonged to the Rev. Edward Holyoke (1689-1769), President of Harvard College from 1737 to 1769. An important form in the seventeenth and early eighteenth centuries, the caudle cup was used at baptisms, weddings, funerals, and celebrations. Bailey's dictionary of 1728 defines caudle as "a Confection made of Ale, or Wine, Sugar, or Spices, to be drank hot." Many caudle cups have survived because they were often willed to the Church for use as communion vessels. Along with sugar or sweetmeat boxes, caudle cups were decorated in a manner unusually elaborate for the period. A caudle cup identical to the *Holyoke Cup* exists in the Museum of Fine Arts, Boston (Bequest Edward J. Holmes, 65.388; Phillips, VIIIb).

John Coney, perhaps the most accomplished and prolific silversmith in America around the turn of the eighteenth century, produced a wide variety of pieces. His early work, such as the *Holyoke Cup,* reflected the English Stuart mode of ornament. Coney was an important member of the Boston community. He served as constable and tithingman, and he engraved the first paper money used in the Colonies. Harvard College paid him 2£ 2s 6d "for a seal for the use of the College," and he produced plate for members of the academic community.

AJM

173 *Two-handled Covered Cup, "The Stoughton Cup,"* 1701

Silver, height 10 inches, diameter lip 7 inches, weight 47 ounces 15 dwt.

Marks: "IC" above a fleur-de-lys, in a heart-shaped punch, on side bearing inscription.

Engraved by Coney with the Stoughton arms in acanthus mantling, and inscribed on the other side in another hand: The Gift of the Hon. William Stoughton, who died at Dorchester, July 7th, 1701

Provenance: Harvard University, Gift of William Stoughton, 1701 (877.1927).

Bibliography: H. F. Clark, *John Coney, Silversmith, 1655-1722,* Boston and New York, 1932, 30-31, pl. 10; Harvard University, *Furniture and Decorative Arts of the Period 1636-1836* [exhibition catalogue, Harvard Tercentenary Exhibition], Cambridge, Mass., 1936, no. 101, pl. 20; J. M. Phillips, *American Silver,* New York, 1949, 52-53, pl. XX; K. C. Buhler, "Harvard College Plate," *The Connoisseur Year Book,* 1955, 53-54, no. iv; K. C. Buhler and G. Hood, *American Silver: Garvan and Other Collections in the Yale University Art Gallery,* New Haven, 1970, 65; G. Hood, *American Silver: A History of Style, 1650-1900,* London and New York, 1971, 59, fig. 47.

From about 1700 to 1715 Boston silversmiths occasionally incorporated into their designs the baroque motifs and patterns of the English William and Mary style. The new style reflected an increased interest on the part of New England patrons in English fashions in the decorative arts. In this two-handled covered cup, contrasting surface richness is achieved by the counterpoise of elegant curves and straight lines and by the placement of embossed bands of fluting and gadrooning on the body and the cover. Impressive in its size and elaborate ornamentation, the *Stoughton Cup* illustrates Coney's preference for and skillful casting of scrolled handles with graduated beading and caryatid grips. The only other surviving contemporary example of this cup form is a vessel by Edward Winslow (Boston, 1669–1753), in the Garvan Collection, Yale University Art Gallery (Mabel Brady Garvan Collection, 1932.47; Buhler and Hood, *American Silver,* fig. 57).

The Winslow cup rests on a higher foot and has hollow handles. Of slightly different proportions and ornamentation, both cups exhibit the surface richness and brilliant technical mastery associated with the early eighteenth-century baroque style.

In his diary of 1701, Judge Samuel Sewall describes a visit paid to the ailing Lieutenant Governor Stoughton, during which Stoughton entrusted the cup to him to confer to the College:

Monday, June 30. Lt. Gov[r]. said would go to the Commencement once more in his life-time; so would adjourn the Court to Friday; and did so. But was very much pained going home. Mr. Nelsen, Secretary and I visit him on Thursday to dissuade him from going, lest some ill consequence should happen. He consented, and order'd us to present his Bowl. After Dinner and singing, I took it and had it fill'd up, and drunk to the president, saying that by reason of the absence of him who was the Firmament and Ornament of the Province, and that Society I presented that Grace-Cup pro more Academarium in Anglia.

AJM

Joseph Kneeland 1698–1760

174 *Pair of Tankards with Hinged, Dome Covers,
"The Vassal Tankards,"* 1729

Silver, height 6¾ inches, diameter base 4¹³⁄₁₆
inches, weight 19 ounces 19 dwt. each

Marks: "Kneeland" in an oblong punch below
lip, near handle

Engraved with the Vassal arms in acanthus
and scroll mantling on the front, and inscribed
in semi-script on the bottom: Donum Joanius
Vassal/Commensalis/ A.D. 1729; Donum Guli-
elmi Vassal/Commensalis/1729

Provenance: Harvard University, Gift of John
and William Vassal, 1729 (874.1927).

Bibliography: Harvard University, *Furniture
and Decorative Arts of the Period 1636–1836*
[exhibition catalogue, Harvard Tercentenary
Exhibition], Cambridge, Mass., 1936, no. 134,
pl. 23; F. B. Robinson, "The Vassal Tankards,"
Harvard Alumni Bulletin, 38, 1935, 82–84; K. C.
Buhler, "Harvard College Plate," *The Connoisseur Year Book,* 1955, 55–56, no. viii.

The straight, sloping sides and broad, smooth
surfaces of the *Vassal Tankards* exemplify the
Queen Anne style, which superseded the earlier, more lavish mode. The simplicity of the
Queen Anne style, misleadingly titled as the
fashion did not attain universal popularity until after Queen Anne's death, constituted a
reaction to the baroque style, typified by the
Stoughton Cup. In the place of elaborate decorative ornament, the silver material itself,
worked into simple shapes, enhanced by narrow mouldings and sparse cast ornaments, became the chief source of admiration.

In the design of the *Vassal Tankards,* Kneeland effectively combined smooth surfaces,
simple mouldings, including strengthening
midbands, and hollow handles with the engraved embellishment of the acanthus and
scroll mantling enclosing the Vassal arms.

John Vassal, Class of 1732, and William Vassal, Class of 1733, were born in the West Indies
and were admitted to Harvard College as Fellow Commoners in 1729. The Harvard faculty
records of 18 October 1729 note: "Agre'd yt
Vassal Sophimore and Vassal Fresh-man be
admitted Fellow-Commoners." Fellow Commoners paid higher rates and were granted
extra privileges. In accordance with university
traditions, Fellow Commoners also contributed tankards, such as these by the little-
known Boston silversmith Joseph Kneeland,
and other forms of plate to the University.

AJM

Paul Revere 1735–1818

175 *Pair of Casters,* ca. 1790

Silver, height to top of finial 5⅞ inches, 6 inches, weight 3 ounces 14 dwt. 20 grams, 3 ounces 18 dwt.

Marks: "PR" in script in rectangle

Engraved with a crest of a hen and inscribed on the bottom: EW to LW

Provenance: Mrs. Frederic Hewitt; Mrs. Ernest G. Stillman; Fogg Art Museum, Harvard University, Gift of Mrs. Ernest G. Stillman (1927.1–2).

Bibliography: Harvard University, *Furniture and Decorative Arts of the Period 1636–1836* [exhibition catalogue, Harvard Tercentenary Exhibition], Cambridge, Mass., 1936, no. 158.

Paul Revere learned his trade from his father né Apollos Rivoire, who had apprenticed with John Coney. The younger Revere's versatile activities included printing, engraving, working in brass, iron, and copper, goldsmithing, silversmithing, dentistry, and harness-making, as well as his renowned patriotic services. Revere's oeuvre in silver spans a variety of styles, from the imported rococo manner of Thomas Chippendale to the neoclassical Federal Style.

The pair of casters in the Fogg Collection typifies Revere's post-Revolutionary use of the urn shape and bright-cut ornament, achieved by gouging a series of lines, rather than engraving a continuous line. Typical of Revere's work in the late 1780's and the 1790's are the engraved floral festoons and the elegant, restrained outline of the casters, with their square plinths, urn-shaped bodies, and domed covers with concave sections. Both the shapes and the decoration preferred by Revere ca. 1790 suggest the influence on American decorative arts of the designs of the brothers Adam and such cabinet-makers as Sheraton and Hepplewhite (cf. K. C. Buhler, *Paul Revere, Goldsmith 1735–1818,* Boston, 1956, figs. 46 a-b, 49, 60, 64). The casters must antedate 1795, when Revere abandoned the mark "PR" in script. Urn-shaped pepper and spice casters such as these would have been paired with oval pierced silver and blue glass salts.

AJM

Obadiah Rich silversmith 1808–1888

Attributed to Horatio Greenough, sculptor and designer, 1805–1852

176 *Inkstand,* ca. 1830

Silver, height 5⅝ inches, width base 3⅝ inches, weight 27.2 ounces

Marks: "O. Rich," "Boston," "fine" on the bottom of the base

Provenance: Andrews Norton(?); Mrs. William Norton Bullard; Fogg Art Museum, Harvard University, Bequest of Mrs. William Norton Bullard (1961.111).

Bibliography: M. G. Fales, "Obadiah Rich, Boston Silversmith," *Antiques,* 94, October 1968, 567–568, fig. 2; K. C. Buhler and G. Hood, *American Silver: Garvan and Other Collections in the Yale University Art Gallery,* New Haven, 1970, 226.

Supported by three acanthus scrolls bolted to a flat tripod plinth, an urn-shaped well with a pointed drop contains its original blown-glass ink bottle. Decorative motifs, such as the greyhounds' heads applied to the side of the well, the egg moulding of the cover, and the bound leaves of the bobèche, exhibit technical virtuosity in casting and chasing. The quality is typical of Obadiah Rich's craftsmanship. Rich produced a wide variety of pieces during the two decades of a successful career, tragically truncated when he become blind in 1850. In all probability, he created the inkstand at the start of his career, before he turned his talents to reviving Queen Anne and rococo forms. The Garvan Collection of the Yale University Art Gallery contains another version of the tripod inkstand, somewhat less harmonious in proportions (Mabel Brady Garvan Collection 1934.374, Buhler and Hood, *American Silver,* fig. 326). Whereas the bezel-edged cover of the Fogg piece is clearly original, the candlestick cover and milled flange of the Yale version appear to be inferior later additions.

Traditionally, Horatio Greenough is credited with the design of the inkstand. Although Greenough only spent about three years altogether in America after his graduation from Harvard College (1825), he received numerous commissions from Bostonians passing through Florence, where he resided for most of the rest of his life. His ties with Harvard friends and faculty members remained strong, and it is indeed conceivable that he might have produced drawings for this inkstand as a favor for Prof. Andrews Norton.

Clearly, the sophisticated design of the piece indicates the hand of an artist deeply concerned with achieving a unity of geometrical and decorative forms. Although Obadiah Rich personally designed certain pieces, his approach usually involved either conventional application of ornamental bands to standard vessel shapes or creative copying of famous European models (cf. the *Webster Vase,* 1835, Boston Public Library; Fales, *Antiques,* fig. 1). On the other hand, Greenough's rigorous academic training, as well as his understanding of architectural principles, would have enabled him to create such an original synthesis. Specific motifs, such as the hounds' heads, relate directly to works by Greenough (cf. the statue "Arno," ca. 1838; N. Wright, *Horatio Greenough, The First American Sculptor,* Philadelphia, 1963, ill. 340). Because of the dignity of the forms and the masterful handling of the medium, the piece attains monumentality despite its diminutive size.

AJM

An Abbreviated Inventory of American Art in the Collections of
Harvard University

This selection of some of the most interesting works from Harvard University holdings in American paintings, drawings, watercolors, and sculpture represents only a tiny fraction of the whole collection. Only those works accessioned after 1936 have been included from the Harvard University Portrait Collection. Works accessioned before that date can be found in Laura Huntsinger, *Harvard Portraits* (Alan Burroughs, ed, Cambridge, Mass., 1936). The catalogue number is given for those works included in the exhibition. The specific Harvard departmental collection to which the work belongs is indicated by abbreviation; works in the collection of the Fogg Art Museum are indicated by the abbreviation FAM and the appropriate accession number.

Fogg Art Museum	FAM
Harvard University Portrait Collection	HUP
Graduate School of Business Administration	GBA
Houghton Library	HL
Peabody Museum	PM
Museum of Comparative Zoology	MCZ
Law School	LS
Medical School	MS

Paintings

Allston, Washington

	Portrait of Benjamin West	FAM 1943.126
	Portrait of Loammi Baldwin, Jr.	FAM 1955.168
30	*Diana in the Chase*	FAM 1956.62
	The Sisters	FAM 1957.1
	Portrait of Samuel Coleridge	HL
	Self Portrait at College	FAM 5.1955
	Rebecca at the Well	FAM 7.1955

Anuszkiewicz, Richard

	The Source of Fire	FAM 1967.73

Audubon, John James

41	*Wild Turkey Cock and Hen and Nine Chicks*	FAM 1964.146
40	*Blackcock*	FAM 1964.147

Avery, Milton

	Bright Day Vermont	FAM 1962.193
154	*Still Life with Woman*	FAM 1966.85

Badger, Joseph

4	*Rev. George Whitefield*	HUP H 27
	Edmund Trowbridge	LS

Bayer, Herbert

	Verdure	FAM 1950.106
	Verdure	FAM 1950.169

Baziotes, William

155	*Bird of Paradise*	FAM 1949.51

Benton, Thomas Hart

	Nude Drying Herself	FAM 1929.101

Bierstadt, Albert

74	*Rocky Mountains*	FAM 1895.698
76	*Portrait of John Tyndall*	FAM 1939.185
75	*Landscape*	FAM 1940.299
	The Trout Brook	FAM 1953.60

Bingham, George Caleb

47	*Concealed Enemy*	PM 41-72-10/28

Blackburn, Joseph

	Rev. Daniel Greenleaf	HUP H 468

Blakelock, Ralph Albert

	Landscape	FAM 1935.20
	Landscape	FAM 1929.102

Bloom, Hyman

	Nude Youth Bending Forward	FAM 1936.73
	Portrait of a Boy in White Shirt	FAM 1936.76
	Youth Bending Forward	FAM 1936.77
	Portrait of Allen Parker	FAM 1936.78
	Portrait of Allen Parker	FAM 1936.79
	Self Portrait	FAM 1936.80
	Half Figure of Charlie Parker	FAM 1936.81
	Portrait of Allen Parker	FAM 1936.82
	Seated Youth	FAM 1936.150

Blume, Peter
Passage to Aetna — FAM 1958.84
Preliminary Sketch for Passage to Aetna — FAM 1960.724
Oil Sketch for Passage to Aetna — FAM 1960.723

Bromley, H. Thomas
91 *Still Life with Duck* — FAM 1961.155

Cassatt, Mary
Woman and Children — FAM 1922.28
88 *Girl on Settee with Black Dog* — FAM 1961.159

Cavallon, Giorgio
Untitled — FAM 1966.95

Chase, William M.
Rutherford B. Hayes — LS
Portrait of Edward Everett Hale — FAM 1955.19

Church, Frederick E.
Landscape — FAM 1940.301

Cole, Thomas
Landscape (verso: Watkin's Glen) — FAM 1966.164
44 *House, Mt. Desert, Maine* — FAM 1956.222

Copley, John Singleton
Monmouth before James II — FAM 1917.67
Portrait of Dorothy Murray — FAM 1929.321
9 *John Adams* — HUP H 74
8 *Nicholas Boylston* — HUP H 90
7 *Mrs. Thomas Boylston* — HUP H 16
Portrait of Colonel Dachenhausen — FAM 1942.178
Portrait of Major General de la Motte — FAM 1942.179
10 *Portrait of Hugo and Schleppengrell* — FAM 1942.180
Portrait of Major General de la Motte — FAM 1942.181
Portait of Benjamin West — FAM 1943.128
Sketch for the Death of Chatham — FAM 1943.1839
Charles I Demanding Impeachment of Five Members of the House of Common — FAM 1957.224
Engraved Key to the Painting of the Death of Chatham — FAM 1943.1839b
12 *Monmouth before James II* — FAM 1957.225

Davies, Arthur B.
Flourishing Summer — FAM 1957.46

Davis, Charles H.
Landscape, Brilliant Sunset Clouds — FAM 1927.213
Rural Landscape — FAM 1949.124

Deas, Charles
Ft. Snelling — PM 41–72–10/69

Doughty, Thomas
Industrial Landscape — GBA

Dunlap, William
Gabriel Duval — LS
Portrait of Anne Grant — FAM 1935.32

Durand, Asher
James Kent — LS

Duveneck, Frank
95 *Study of Woman's Head* — FAM 1943.30

Eakins, Thomas
The Critic, Francis J. Ziegler — FAM 1943.130
113 *Portrait of a Young Woman* — FAM 1969.1

Earl, Ralph
Portrait of Reuben H. Booth — FAM 1943.131

Eastman, Seth
Squaws Playing Ball on the Prairie — PM 41–72–10/71
Eta Keazah, a Sisseton Sioux — PM 41–72–10/74
50 *Live Oaks with Two Small Figures* — PM 41–72–10/75
Medicine Dance of the Dakcotah or Sioux — PM 41–72–10/76
Unidentified Fort (attrib. to) — PM 41–72–10/518
Indians, River Banks (attrib. to) — PM 41–72–10/519
Two Others — PM

Eilshemius, Louis M.
The Two Birds — FAM 1950.44
Slender Tree — FAM 1957.155
Water Nymph — FAM 1963.123
The White Horse — FAM 1964.143

Feke, Robert
Stephen Sewall — LS
5 *Isaac Royall and His Family* — HUP H 159

Fisher, Alvan
View of Harvard College — President's Office
View of Harvard College — President's Office
35 *Landscape* — GBA
Landscape with Horses and Men — GBA

Fleischer, Max
Celluloids from Gulliver's Travels — FAM 1940.6–7

Frothingham, James
Benjamin Waterhouse — HUP H 502

Furness, William Henry, Jr.
Portrait of a Girl — FAM 1949.134

Gerry, Samuel L.
Washington's Tomb — FAM 1957.174

Gifford, Sanford R.
72 *Storm King on the Hudson (attrib. to)* — FAM 1895.703
80 *Leander's Tower on the Bosphorus* — FAM 1895.716

Greenleaf, Benjamin
27 *Dr. Cotton Tufts* — MS

Hall, George Henry
Grapes — FAM 1895.675

Harding, Chester
62 *Dr. Francis Parkman* — HUP H 132
Asabel Sterns — LS

Maurer, Alfred Henry		
Landscape	FAM 1969.178	
Miller, Alfred J.		
49 *Crow Indian on the Lookout*	PM 41–72–10/442	
Landscape with Indian Figures	PM 41–72–10/440	
Morse, Samuel Finley Breese		
Jedidiah Morse	FAM 1943.142	
36 *Mrs. Jedidiah Morse*	FAM 1943.143	
Motherwell, Robert		
Wall Painting	FAM 1959.18	
156 *Elegy*	FAM 1949.49	
Collage No. 1	FAM 1949.50	
Noland, Kenneth		
Hover	FAM 1964.35	
164 *Karma*	FAM 1965.22	
Page, William		
Joseph Story	LS	
Peale, Charles Willson		
Samuel Chase	LS	
15 *Portrait of George Washington*	FAM 1943.144	
Portrait of an Unknown Lady of Maryland	FAM 1943.145	
Portrait of Thomas McKean	FAM 1943.146	
16 *George Washington (miniature)*	HL MS AM 1375	
Peale, James		
17 *Portrait of a Young Girl*	FAM 1943.147	
Peale, Rembrandt		
18 *Jared Sparks*	HUP H 244	
Portrait of McKean Buchanan	FAM 1943.148	
Petticolas, Philip A.		
Portrait of George Washington (miniature)	FAM 1949.93	
Phillips, Ammi		
Portrait of Harriet Leavens	FAM 1945.27	
Pollock, Jackson		
157 *No. 2, 1950*	FAM 1965.554	
Pratt, Matthew		
Daniel Horsmander	LS	
Richards, William Trost		
Seascape	FAM 1954.28	
Rimmer, William		
78 *To the Charge*	FAM 1936.10.1	
Portrait of Rev. Calvin Hitchcock	FAM 1948.55	
Ross, Denman		
Many works in the Fogg Collection	FAM	
Rothko, Mark		
Five Paintings	Holyoke Center	

Rubenstein, Lewis		
Structure	FAM 1935.33	
Framed Fresco	FAM 1935.34	
Unframed Fresco	FAM	
Sander, Ludwig		
Untitled	FAM 1972.1	
Sargent, John Singer		
119 *Lake O'Hara*	FAM 1916.496	
Gog and Magog	FAM 1933.155	
The Unveiling of Truth	FAM 1933.156	
Study for Revenge	FAM 1939.91	
Portrait of Miss Elsie Palmer	FAM 1942.58	
Courtyard of San Giovanni Evangelista	FAM 1942.187	
Head of a Sicilian Girl	FAM 1943.149	
116 *Breakfast Table*	FAM 1943.150	
Portrait of Johannes Wolff	FAM 1943.151	
Study for "El Jaleo"	FAM 1943.152	
115 *The Musicians, Study for "El Jaleo"*	FAM 1943.153	
View of Simplon Valley	FAM 1943.155	
Portrait of Laura Lister	FAM 1943.156	
16 oil sketches	FAM	
Savage, Edward		
22 *George Washington*	HUP H 49	
Sheeler, Charles		
143 *Upper Deck*	FAM 1933.97	
Soyer, Moses		
Tap Dance Studio	FAM 1962.206	
Soyer, Raphael		
Two Girls	FAM 1946.8	
Stuart, Gilbert		
25 *Mrs. Israel Thorndike, Jr.*	HUP H 555	
Portrait of Samuel K. Williams	FAM 1954.100	
26 *Portrait of J. Q. Adams (painted w/Sully)*	HUP H 187	
Portrait of Elizabeth Winslow Williams	FAM 1954.101	
Portrait of Lord John Hamilton	FAM 1959.154	
23 *Portrait of George Washington*	HUP H 631	
Portrait of George Washington	FAM 1960.116	
24 *Medallion Portrait of Thomas Jefferson*	FAM 1960.156	
Portrait of William Porter	FAM 1971.20	
Edward Everett	HUP H 528	
Josiah Quincy	HUP H 581	
William Hale	HUP H 517	
Portrait of a Man	FAM 1898.140	
John Clark Howard	MS	
Theodore Sedgwick (attrib. to)	LS	
Sully, Thomas		
42 *John McAllister, Jr.*	FAM 1943.157	
43 *Mrs. John McAllister, Jr.*	FAM 1943.158	

Burchfield, Charles
Landscape, August Sunlight FAM 1930.463
148 *Old Farm House, September Sunlight* FAM 1933.28
149 *March Sunlight* FAM 1934.63
Study for July FAM 1954.14

Cadmus, Paul
Scroll of Birchbark FAM 1958.10
Inventor FAM 1965.107
Study of a Male Head FAM 1971.32

Calder, Alexander
Hippopotamus FAM 1965.444

Cassatt, Mary
Mother and Child FAM 1943.569

Catlin, George
Hongs-Kay-Dee PM 41–72–10/62
48 *Wan-ee-ton* PM 41–72–10/63
Mah-To-Toh-Pah PM 41–72–10/64

Champney, Benjamin
54 *Mountain Landscape* FAM 1898.443
Scene on the Connecticut FAM 1898.442
Two Sketchbooks FAM 1960.166–167

Colman, Samuel
Morning-glories FAM 1895.669

Copley, John Singleton
Mother and Child (attrib. to) FAM 1898.131
11 *Study for Central Figure in Monmouth before
James II* FAM 1933.1
*Portrait of Mrs. John Scollay (Mercy
Greenleaf)* FAM 1943.570

Davidson, Jo
Portrait of Anatole France FAM 1955.57

Davies, Arthur B.
Study of a Female Nude Seated FAM 1955.56
Sketch of Standing Female Nude FAM 1955.57

Davis, Stuart
Davits FAM 1965.111

Demuth, Charles
135 *Lily* FAM 1925.5.1
Fruit and Daisies FAM 1925.5.2
136 *Fruit and Sunflowers* FAM 1925.5.3
In the Gymnasium FAM 1949.10
Head of a Woman FAM 1956.51

Dewing, Thomas
Standing Woman in Green Skirt FAM 1941.75

Dickinson, Preston
Still Life FAM 1927.20
Self Portrait FAM 1965.112

Dove, Arthur G.
Gas Tank and Building 38 FAM 1971.3

Dunlap, William
Portrait of Captain Caleb Coggeshill FAM 1943.517

Eastman, Seth
51 *Winnebago Wigwams* PM 41–72–10/118
135 watercolors and drawings PM 41–72–10/71–206

Eilshemius, Louis M.
Sketchbook FAM 1946.23
Sie wird doch da sein FAM 1965.113
Kinder lallen FAM 1965.14
24 drawings and studies FAM 1946.22.1–24

Fisher, Alvan
View of Harvard College FAM 1968.17
34 *Three Views of Harvard Yard* HL

Flavin, Dan
Portrait of Edward Munch FAM 1966.65
A New One, #3 FAM 1966.66

Flannagan, John B.
Lifeguard FAM 1946.61

Frazier, John R.
Portrait of a Man Seated in a Chair FAM 1931.251

Gabo, Naum
Composition FAM 1957.58

Gay, Walter
Interior of a Room FAM 1950.116

Graham, John
Equestrian FAM 1966.10
Portrait of Madame Sijou FAM 1966.11

Grosz, George
Sketchbook FAM 1955.95
The Junker Officer FAM 1955.96
The Street Cleaners FAM 1955.97

Harnett, William M.
90 *Head of a Woman* FAM 1965.120

Hartley, Marsden
The Little Arroya Sundown FAM 1950.45
Mr. Katahdin FAM 1961.123
Still Life of Fruit FAM 1971.2

Haseltine, William Stanley
Fishing Boats on Beach FAM 1936.144
Olive Grove at Tivoli FAM 1936.145

Hassam, Childe
Little Church around the Corner FAM 1941.60
Portrait of a Girl, Julia FAM 1941.61
Portrait of a Girl, Harriette FAM 1941.62
Spring in Charleston FAM 1941.63
St. Philips in Charleston FAM 1941.64

Vedder, Elihu
Girl Walking Down Stairs   FAM 1941.76

Weber, Max
Female Torso   FAM 1957.14
Venice   FAM 1965.158
Italian Landscape   FAM 1965.159
Interior of a Church   FAM 1965.160
Seated Figure   FAM 1965.161

Weir, J. Alden
Hollyhocks   FAM 1943.324
Roses   FAM 1943.325
Hunter's Dog and Gun   FAM 1943.326

West, Benjamin
14 *Fidelia and Spiranza*   FAM 1943.329

Whistler, James Abbott McNeil
Sunday at Domberg   FAM 1917.5
Maud Reading in a Hammock   FAM 1943.330
Miss Leyland   FAM 1943.605
Riva Degli Schiavoni at Sunset   FAM 1943.617
27 others   FAM

Wimar, Carl
52 *Mounted Indians Running Buffalo*   PM 4–72–10/516
Drawings and watercolors   PM 41–72–10/514–515

Wyeth, Andrew
Teal's House   FAM 1964.70
Study of Beach Tree Trunks   FAM 1970.100

Sculpture

Bartlett, Paul Wayland
Torso of a Woman   FAM 1947.27
Bust of Alexander Agassiz   FAM 1953.85

Baskin, Leonard
Blind Man   FAM 1970.137
Thracis   FAM 1970.138

Borglum, Gutzon
127 *Marble Head*   FAM 1942.154

Calder, Alexander
158 *Little Blue under Red*   FAM 1955.99

Dallin, Cyrus E.
The Great Spirit   GBA
Indian on Horseback   GBA

Davidson, Jo
133 *Portrait Bust of Joffre*   FAM 1943.1390
Portrait Bust of General Pershing   FAM 1943.1391
Portrait Bust of Clemenceau   FAM 1943.1393
Portrait Bust of Foch   FAM 1943.1394

Dexter, Henry
65 *Mrs. Percival Lowell Everett*   FAM 1939.82

Duveneck, Frank
96 *Charles William Eliot*   HUP S 85
Ralph Waldo Emerson   HUP B 20

Flannagan, John B.
Mother and Child   FAM 1940.51

Fraser, James Earle
Rough Rider   GBA

French, Daniel Chester
Lincoln Standing   FAM 1943.1107
125 *Lincoln Seated*   FAM 1943.1108
124 *Spirit of the Waters*   FAM 1943.1361
Benediction   FAM 1943.1810
Ralph Waldo Emerson   HUP S 8
William Francis Bartlett   HUP S 17
Charles Russell Lowell   HUP S 18

Greenough, Horatio
Head of Christ   FAM 1969.75
John Warren   HUP S 98
John Collins Warren   HUP S 97
John Warren   HUP S 46
John Collins   HUP S 47
Samuel Appleton   HUP S 14
George Haywood   HUP B 2

Gross, Chaim
Woman's Head   FAM 1962.247
Little Girl   FAM 1962.248

Hadzi, Dimitri
Samurai   FAM 1971.100

Hazeltine, Herbert		
Shire Stallion: Field Marshall V	FAM 1938.8	
The Percheron	FAM 1943.1109	
Held, John		
Standing Horse	FAM 1955.111	
Calf	FAM 1955.112	
Rabbit	FAM 1955.113	
Hoffman, Malvina		
Oriental Figure Seated on Tripod	FAM 1943.822	
Head of Anna Pavlova with Headdress	FAM 1943.1110	
Vita Nuova	FAM 1943.1111	
Bust of Japanese Woman	FAM 1943.1112	
Sacrifice	HUP S 93	
Humphriss, Charles		
121 *Appeal to Manito*	GBA	
The Chief	GBA	
Huntington, Anna Hyatt		
151 *Speedy*	FAM 1943.1845	
Diana	FAM 1927.24	
Kelly, Ellsworth		
Red Blue Sculpture	Peabody Terrace	
Lachaise, Gaston		
142 *Floating Woman*	FAM 1950.113	
141 *"Acrobat"*	FAM 1962.78	
Portrait Bust of e. e. cummings	FAM 1969.160	
Lewis, Edmonia		
61 *Bust of Longfellow*	HUP S 52	
Lipchitz, Jacques		
Bather	FAM 1960.745	
Lippold, Richard		
Study for the Tree of Life	FAM 1950.170	
Manship, Paul		
Wrestlers	FAM 1928.163	
Centaur and Nymph	FAM 1928.164	
Sarah Janet (Manship)	FAM 1943.1035	
Celestial Sphere	FAM 1943.1113	
Armillary Sphere	FAM 1943.1362	
Ashtray-Centaur	FAM 1943.1308	
Miles, Emily Winthrop		
12 works	FAM	
Mirko, Basaldella		
Personaggio	FAM 1965.60	
Nadelman, Elie		
132 *Pianiste*	FAM 1956.200	
Nevelson, Louise		
Figure	FAM 1970.141	

Powers, Hiram		
57 *Luly's Hand*	FAM 1928.115	
58 *America*	FAM 1958.180	
Benjamin Franklin	FAM 1961.27	
Jared Sparks	HUP S 5	
John Parker, Jr.	HUP S 10	
James Russell Lowell	HUP S 20	
56 *John Farrar*	HUP S 28	
60 *Henry Wadsworth Longfellow*	HUP S 33	
59 *Robert Charles Winthrop*	HUP S 36	
Liberty	HUP S 86	
Pratt, Bela Lyon		
114 *Bather*	FAM 1939.308	
George Cheyne Shattuck	HUP S 45	
Henry J. Bigelow	HUP S 38	
Jacob Bigelow	HUP S 39	
Henry P. Bowditch	HUP S 53	
Charles Montraville Green	HUP S 73	
Oliver Wendell Holmes	HUP S 42	
John Homans	HUP B 11	
John Barnard Swett Jackson	HUP S 43	
Theobald Smith	HUP S 72	
John Ware	HUP S 10	
Benjamin Waterhouse	HUP S 48	
Phillips Brooks	HUP B 18	
Rogers, John		
70 *Council of War*	HL	
Taking the Oath and Drawing Rations	FAM 1924.79	
Rogers, Randolph		
68 *Nydia*	FAM 1922.136	
Saint-Gaudens, Augustus		
Relief Portrait of Mariana Griswold van Rensselaer	FAM 1923.36	
110 *Standing Lincoln with Chair*	FAM 1943.1116	
Study for the Head of "Diana"	FAM 1961.168	
Relief Portrait of Asa Gray	HUP B 16	
111 *Robert Louis Stevenson*	HL	
Sargent, John Singer		
Model for Crucifix	FAM 1933.45c	
The Crucifix	FAM 1943.1117	
Schreyvogel, Charles		
123 *The Last Drop*	GBA	
Stankiewicz, Richard		
Figure	FAM 1970.142	
Sullivan, Louis		
Architectural Ornament	FAM 1965.73	
Architectural Ornament	FAM 1963.164	